PERSONAL POWER

How to fulfil your
private and professional life

Jenny Mosley &
Eileen Gillibrand

Positive Press

Published by Positive Press
8 Westbourne Road
Trowbridge
Wiltshire BA14 0AJ
England

First published by Jenny Mosley Consultancies 1993
New impression with amendments under Positive Press imprint © 2001

ISBN 0 9530122 3 9

Printed in England

How to use this Workbook

This workbook has been written for women who want to fulfil their personal and professional lives. It is a self-development programme that has been designed for you to use on your own. However working with a friend or a colleague is always beneficial and we do suggest that you discuss your ideas and practise the exercises with other people whenever possible.

The sections focus on building self-esteem, dealing with stress, developing assertive relationships and managing your lifestyle. They are all inter-related and all contribute to the development of your personal power. The workbook has been flexibly designed so that each part stands alone. However maximum benefit will be gained if you work through the book in sequence since many exercises build on strengths and skills developed in the earlier sections.

Do work through the book at your own pace, organising your study to suit your own needs.

The sections are:

1 Building Self-Esteem in your Private and Professional Life page 3

2 Dealing with Stress in your Private and Professional Life page 57

3 Developing Assertiveness in your Private and Professional Life page 105

4 Managing your Private and Professional Life page 157

   Information about Further Publications and Training page 193

What is Personal Power?

Personal power is an inner power that comes through self-knowledge. Getting to know yourself, learning to judge how you feel, to understand why you think and behave as you do, will enable you to feel more sure of yourself as a person. As your knowledge and belief in yourself grows, so will your confidence, and with it the conviction that you *can* improve your personal and professional life.

Personal power depends on:

☆ recognising what you have to offer
☆ developing these resources in yourself
☆ having the energy and motivation to realise this potential for change and self-fulfilment

Without personal power we may feel lethargic, insecure, angry or frustrated. We are unlikely to fulfil our needs and often lose a sense of vision or direction. We may give other people power over us and allow them to be responsible for what happens to us. Gradually we may begin to believe we don't deserve any better; everyone else appears better qualified for the job; trivial problems become massive obstacles and opportunities are missed.

With personal power we gain real impetus to make things happen. We become inspired and motivated to realise our personal and professional potential – to strive for what *could* be.

This workbook will help you to develop personal power in your own life. The self-development programme contained in the workbook focuses on four key themes:

☆ self-esteem
☆ stress
☆ assertiveness
☆ management skills

You will be guided through a process of self-discovery using questionnaires, information sheets and practical exercises, to explore issues which are personally holding you back. Step-by-step action plans will show you where to make changes in your life where these are needed. It is then up to you to put these into action!

1

Building Self-Esteem in your Private and Professional Life

Building Self-Esteem

Introduction

Your self-esteem affects the choices that you make in your life, how you relate to others and what you think you are capable of achieving.

> *Do you have good self-esteem?*

> *Do you value your strengths and qualities or do you always tend to put yourself down?*

If you suffer from nagging self-doubt and a lack of confidence, you probably have low self-esteem. This will most definitely prevent you from achieving all that you are capable of and stop you fulfilling your true potential.

You need to learn how to develop a positive self-image to improve your chances of success in your personal and professional life.

What is Self-Esteem?

Self-esteem is the 'inner picture' that we hold of ourselves and our limitations and strengths. This self-image has been contributed to by our experiences with other people in the past, i.e. the way we were treated and talked to by our family, our teachers, our friends, work colleagues or even the way 'life' has treated us and the way we then responded to different events, illnesses or lack of advantages.

Good self-esteem

An individual with good self-esteem views herself as a capable, likeable and worthwhile person. She is confident in her ability to succeed, will welcome and enjoy new experiences and will be able to relate well to other people. Her self-confidence and optimism will allow her to adopt a positive approach in all that she does and this will be effective in creating all manner of personal and professional success. Moreover, good self-esteem will enable her to learn from criticism, and mistakes, and failures, and to view them in a calm and realistic way.

Low self-esteem

An individual with low self-esteem, however, can view herself as useless and incompetent. Her lack of confidence can sometimes result in nagging self-doubt, occasional self-pity and an inability to sustain meaningful relationships with others. Her personal view of herself will lead her to believe that this is how others see her and she will react accordingly to protect herself from hurt by either being aggressive and 'putting other people down' or withdrawing into a lonely 'shell'. Secretly she regards herself as a failure or as totally misunderstood and thinks everyone else is more successful than she is. This negative thinking results in a pattern of behaviour which becomes a self-fulfilling prophecy and ensures that she continues to fail.

The importance of developing your self-esteem

Developing good self-esteem should not be confused with selfishness; the latter is a result of low self-esteem. Therefore, a person with good self-esteem is able to spend time on herself without feeling guilty. If an individual can learn to accept and like herself 'faults and all', then she can believe others will accept and love her also. She can approach life in a positive fashion, confident of success, and relate to others in a respecting and caring manner which will, in turn, lead them to respect and care for her.

The building of self-esteem is vital for the realisation of true potential.

Good Self-Esteem Leads to.....

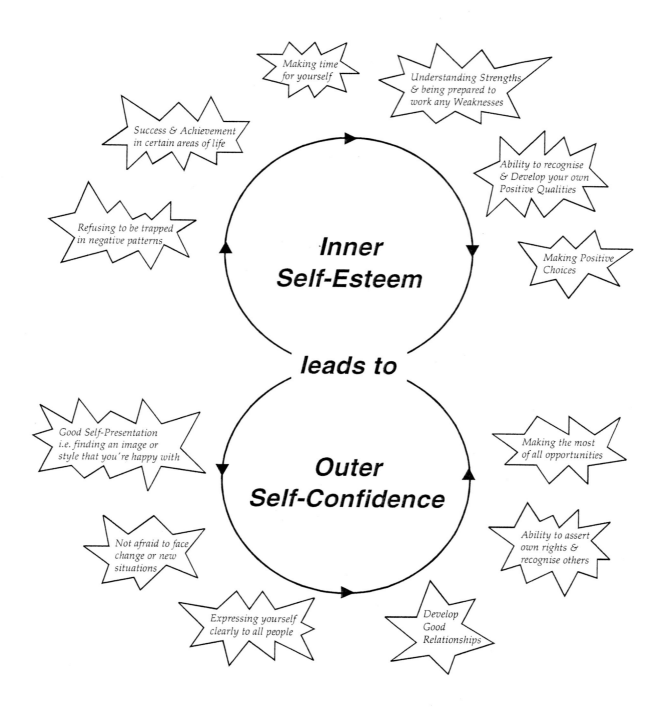

Making time
for yourself

Understanding Strengths
& being prepared to
work any Weaknesses

Success & Achievement
in certain areas of life

Ability to recognise
& Develop your own
Positive Qualities

Refusing to be trapped
in negative patterns

Making Positive
Choices

**Inner
Self-Esteem**

leads to

**Outer
Self-Confidence**

Good Self-Presentation
i.e. finding an image or
style that you're happy with

Making the most
of all opportunities

Not afraid to face
change or new
situations

Ability to assert
own rights &
recognise others

Expressing yourself
clearly to all people

Develop
Good
Relationships

Understanding Self-Esteem in your Private and Professional life

In our past we will all have encountered negative statements that have affected the way we now see ourselves. How many of the following comments sound familiar?

Family	I never had as much as you.
	Why can't you be more like your sister/brother.
	So and so's daughter is so well behaved etc.
	Why are you so clumsy/stupid/lazy/scruffy etc.
	You're completely untrustworthy.
	I don't like your friends.
	If only ......
	Why aren't you .....
	I never had migraines till I had you.
	You're always miserable.
Teachers	You could do better.
	You never stop talking.
	I think even you could do this.
	Why do you always make a mess of things.
	You're such a bad influence.
Friends	I'm not going to be your friend.
	Your house stinks.
	You've got a big nose.
	You're fat/thick/ugly/goofy etc.
Partners	That dress doesn't suit you.
	You don't understand me.
	Why can't you take more of an interest in life?
	Kate (or anyone else) is so pretty/interesting/witty/caring/intelligent/sexy, etc.
	I'd rather go down the pub with my mates.

It is vital to understand some of the statements that have influenced your self-esteem – as self-knowledge empowers you to distance yourself from the past in order to make necessary changes for the future.

Now identify and write down any further comments that directly affected you in the past that have not been mentioned.

Family	
Teachers	
Parents	
Friends	
Partners	

Now take the time to: Understand that if people you consider are important continually make negative statements to you, you will internalise them into negative self-beliefs.

Do you need to tackle anyone in your present life about the way they talk to you?

Private Life

How is your self-esteem?

Put a ✔ *in the appropriate* | box |

	Part A.	Never	Sometimes	Often	Always
1.	Do you view yourself as a likeable and worthwhile person?				
2.	Do you seek out and enjoy new experiences?				
3.	Do you enjoy secure and fulfilling relationships with family and friends?				
4.	Do you have an optimistic approach to life?				
5.	Can you admit to making mistakes?				
6.	Do you consider that you are a capable person?				
7.	Are you happy about meeting new people?				
8.	Do you feel that you are using all your talents and capabilities?				
9.	Do you give yourself treats?				
10.	Do you trust other people?				
11.	Do you experience joy in your life?				
12.	Are you able to relax and have a good time?				

Score: Never 1
          Sometimes 2
          Often 3
          Always 4

	Part B.	Never	Sometimes	Often	Always
13.	Does criticism make you feel totally miserable and/or a failure?				
14.	Are you envious of other women's lives?				
15.	Do you feel other women enjoy more successful relationships than you?				
16.	Do you worry about what people might think of you?				
17.	Do you feel you have to try to 'impress' people with your appearance?				
18.	Do you feel you have to try to 'impress' people with your capabilities?				
19.	Do you feel 'misunderstood' by other people?				
20.	Do you find yourself in situations where you feel excluded?				
21.	Do you find yourself in situations where you feel shy or awkward?				
22.	Do you feel depressed with your life?				
23.	Do you 'miss out' on opportunities to develop areas of your life that you would like to because of outside pressures?				
24.	Do you feel hopeless about your life?				
25.	Do you make excuses for not doing the things you feel you would like to do?				
26.	Do you find yourself, last thing at night, dwelling on all that has gone wrong during the day rather than focusing on something that has gone right?				
27.	Do you try to please other people?				
28.	Do you 'put yourself down' to other people?				
29.	Do you keep problems to yourself?				
30.	Do you secretly dislike people?				

Score: Never 4
           Sometimes 3
           Often 2
           Always 1

Results

Score 30–45	Your self-esteem is generally low so you need to find ways to enhance it in order to enjoy a more fulfilling personal life. Perhaps it is time to realise that you **can** feel good about yourself and learn how to initiate changes in your private life, which will enhance your self-image, your relationships and, in time make you feel happier in yourself.
Score 46–75	Your self-esteem is fluctuating and still needs to be enhanced. You need to feel more confident in your ability to cope and more able to put yourself forward. Perhaps earlier experiences have left you vulnerable in certain areas; this now needs to be recognised and dealt with.
Score 76–104	In general you have quite sound self-esteem, but certain specific areas are still causing you problems and need to be dealt with if you are to feel fully confident about yourself and able to really make the most out of opportunities that come your way.
Score 105–120	You enjoy a high level of self-esteem and are confident in your outlook on life. Perhaps it is now time to set yourself fresh challenges and consider exciting and new initiatives in your quest for personal fulfilment.

Professional Life

Put a ✔ *in the appropriate* box

	Part A.	Never	Sometimes	Often	Always
1.	Are you happy with your work?				
2.	Do you feel appreciated at work?				
3.	Does your job suit your capabilities?				
4.	Do you get on well with colleagues?				
5.	Do you enjoy a good relationship with your boss?				
6.	Are you able to meet work deadlines?				
7.	Are you happy to learn new skills?				
8.	Would you welcome promotion and additional responsibilities?				
9.	Do you feel confident and relaxed at work?				
10.	Can you delegate work confidently to other people?				
11.	Is your work fulfilling and rewarding?				
12.	Do you feel successful at work?				
13.	Do you fit in at work?				
14.	Do you consider your views are important at work?				
15.	Do you feel confident in dealing with work situations?				
16.	Do you feel you are progressing at satisfactory rate?				
17.	Do you have achievable goals that you are aiming for?				
18.	Do you think you are reliable and conscientious?				
19.	Can you deal effectively with disagreements which arise between colleagues and yourself?				
20.	Do you feel that the type of work you do makes you an interesting person?				
21.	Do you feel your boss/colleagues treat you in a respectful manner?				
22.	Do you initiate new ideas/schemes at work?				

Score: Never 1
          Sometimes 2
          Often 3
          Always.................4

	Part B.	Never	Sometimes	Often	Always
23.	Are you alarmed by new tasks?				
24.	Do you worry about the standard of your work?				
25.	Are you anxious about making a mistake in your work?				
26.	Are you envious of other people's roles at work?				
27.	Do you feel other people at work are more favoured than you are?				
28.	Do you worry about work after you have left the workplace?				
29.	Do you complain about situations/events at work?				
30.	Do you think other people have more exciting-interesting jobs?				

Score: Never 4
Sometimes 3
Often 2
Always 1

Results

Score 30–45	Your self-esteem in your workplace is generally low and changes evidently need to be made. Perhaps you are in the wrong job and need to consider a complete change, otherwise you need to sort out the areas where improvements can be made and decide on a plan of action to implement them.
Score 46–75	There are still work areas that need improving in order for you to be fully satisfied with your professional life. Try and isolate the areas of concern that need to be dealt with so that you can be more effective in achieving job satisfaction and success. You still have an unclear picture of all your qualities and are unable to make the most of any opportunities that arise.
Score 76–104	Your self-esteem at work is generally sound so you can concentrate on those areas where you achieved a low score and find ways to make the necessary improvements. Perhaps it is time to set some fresh challenges or learn a new skill and boost your confidence even further.
Score 105–120	Your self-esteem is high and you seem to be brimming with confidence, but have you set yourself sufficiently high goals? Perhaps now is the time to consider a new challenge or seek exciting fresh horizons.

How to Improve Self-Esteem in your Private and Professional Life

Low self-esteem has a profound effect on our lives. It affects the way we view our own ability to respond to certain 'trigger' events or situations. Low self-esteem therefore traps us in a negative cycle of failure, which creates a self-fulfilling prophecy and prevents us from ever leaving the cycle to enjoy any positive progress. The following theoretical models clearly show how practical exercises of thinking and challenging 'old' negative beliefs can enhance self-esteem and subsequently improve the quality of your private and professional life.

Private Life

The Treadmill of Low Self-Esteem

Example: Meeting New People

The Negative Cycle

Negative Self-belief
I'm no good with people

Poor Self Image
Of self:
I'm boring, I can't make small talk
From others:
They pick up on your negative behaviour and comments

Low Expectations
Of self:
I'll never be an interesting person
From others:
They see you as unwelcoming and lacking in warmth

Fewer Opportunities
e.g. I don't think I'll go to the party tonight
From others:
They think you don't look as though you enjoy yourself, so they begin not to include you.

Poor 'Performance' or Skills
Of self:
I'm just useless at talking
I can't think of anything to talk about
From others:
They never get any response from you so they give up trying to engage you in conversion

Reinforced Negative Self-belief
Of self:
Now I know I'm really dull and uninteresting
From others:
They think you are "stand-offish" or reserved and shy and give up on you

Private Life

The Upward Cycle of Good Self-Esteem

Example: Meeting New People

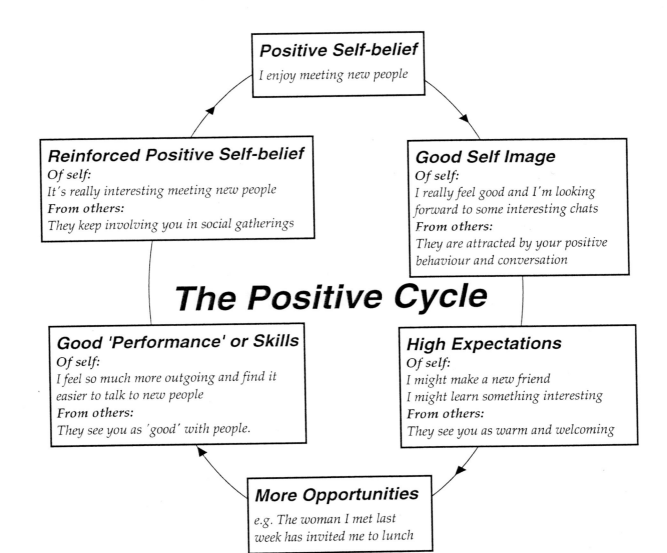

Positive Self-belief
I enjoy meeting new people

Reinforced Positive Self-belief
Of self:
It's really interesting meeting new people
From others:
They keep involving you in social gatherings

Good Self Image
Of self:
I really feel good and I'm looking forward to some interesting chats
From others:
They are attracted by your positive behaviour and conversation

The Positive Cycle

Good 'Performance' or Skills
Of self:
I feel so much more outgoing and find it easier to talk to new people
From others:
They see you as 'good' with people.

High Expectations
Of self:
I might make a new friend
I might learn something interesting
From others:
They see you as warm and welcoming

More Opportunities
e.g. The woman I met last week has invited me to lunch

Professional Life

The Treadmill of Low Self-Esteem

Example: Promotion at Work

Negative Self-belief
I'm not good enough for promotion

Reinforced Negative Self-belief
Of self:
I'll never get on
From others:
They begin to ignore you

Poor Self Image
Of self:
I haven't got what it takes
From others:
They pick up on your negative behaviour and comments

The Negative Cycle

Poor 'Performance' or Skills
Of self:
My work is suffering because I'm bored and lack challenge
From others:
They think you lack enthusiasm and commitment and don't recommend you for promotion

Low Expectations
Of self:
Why would anyone choose me
From others:
They see you as lacking in drive and interest

Fewer Opportunities
e.g. I don't think I'll bother to apply

Professional Life

The Upward Cycle of Good Self-Esteem

Example: Promotion at work

Positive Self-belief

I am good enough to be promoted

Reinforced Positive Self-belief
Of self:
I think I could go a long way
From others:
They think you have so much talent and drive

Good Self Image
Of self:
I'm sure I could do the job
From others:
They pick up on your positive behaviour and comments

The Positive Cycle

Good 'Performance' or Skills
Of self:
I have so much more energy, the new job has really brought 'the best' out of me.
I'm brimming with new ideas and eager to listen to people and learn more
From others:
They see you as having potential for success

High Expectations
Of self:
I would like a new challenge
From others:
They see you as having drive & interest

More Opportunities

e.g. If I get promotion I'll take more responsibility and have the chance to learn more/travel more

Private Life

Choose a situation which holds you back in your own Private Life (e.g. making an official phone call, travelling on your own, organising a party), and fill in the boxes as in the example model.

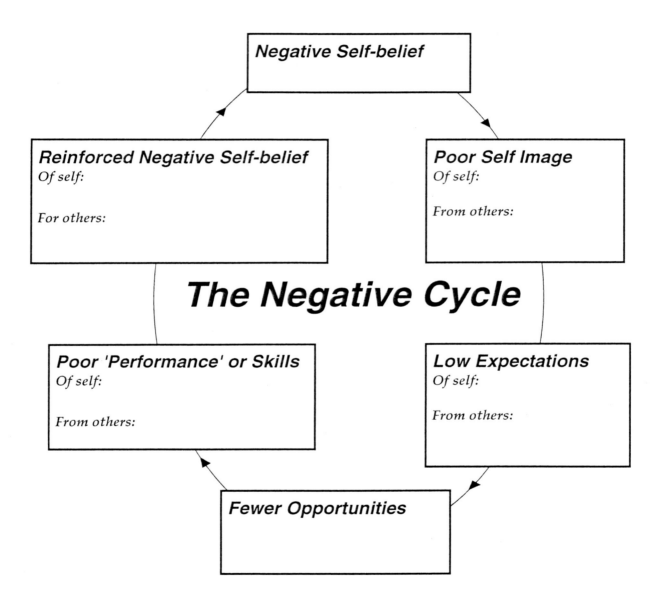

Negative Self-belief

Reinforced Negative Self-belief
Of self:

For others:

Poor Self Image
Of self:

From others:

The Negative Cycle

Poor 'Performance' or Skills
Of self:

From others:

Low Expectations
Of self:

From others:

Fewer Opportunities

Private Life

Now use the same situation to fill in the boxes in the Positive Cycle

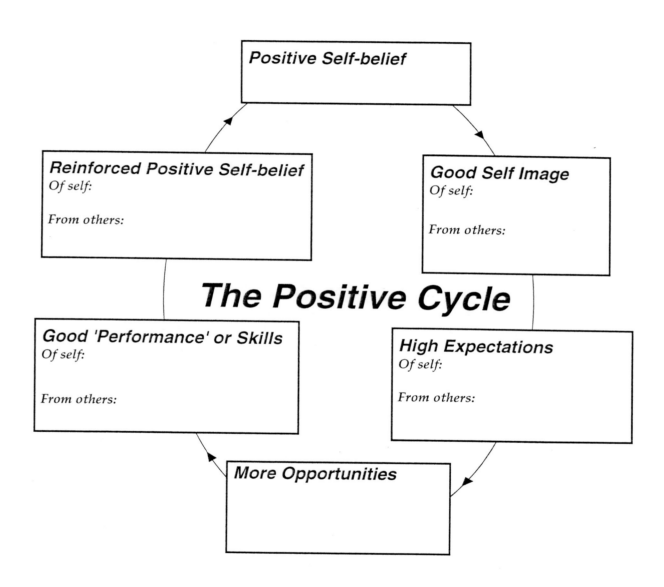

Professional Life

Choose a situation which holds you back in your own Professional Life (e.g. changing your career, dealing with customers or clients, putting forward your ideas).

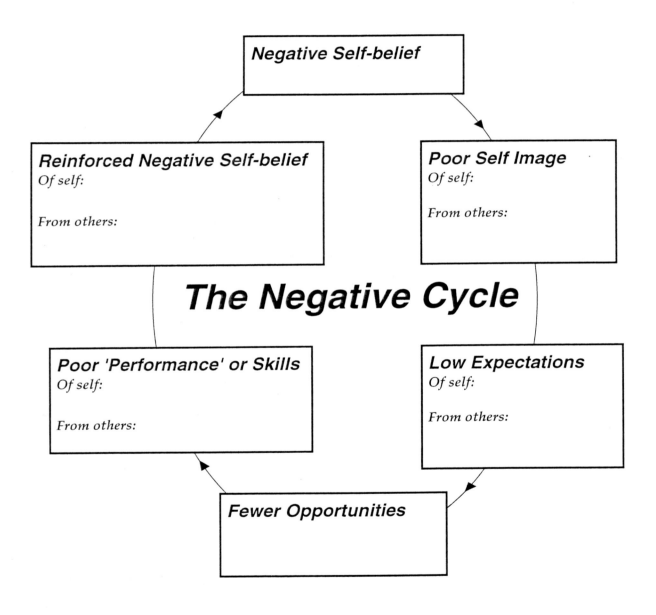

The Negative Cycle

Negative Self-belief

Reinforced Negative Self-belief
Of self:

From others:

Poor Self Image
Of self:

From others:

Poor 'Performance' or Skills
Of self:

From others:

Low Expectations
Of self:

From others:

Fewer Opportunities

Professional Life

Now use the same situation to fill in the boxes in the Positive Cycle

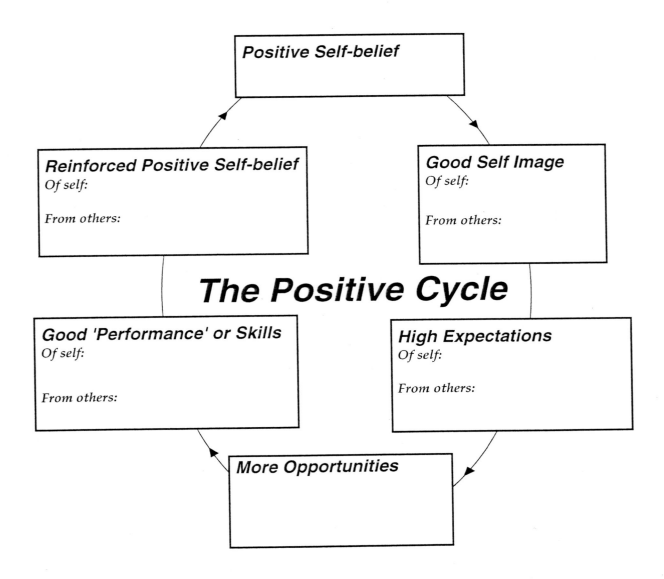

Positive Self-belief

Reinforced Positive Self-belief
Of self:

From others:

Good Self Image
Of self:

From others:

The Positive Cycle

Good 'Performance' or Skills
Of self:

From others:

High Expectations
Of self:

From others:

More Opportunities

Private Life

As you will have seen in the previous exercise, how you react and respond to people and situations greatly influences your experiences in life. Many of the beliefs you hold about yourself can be traced back to your early formative years, but often these beliefs are untrue.

If you cling to mistaken beliefs about yourself, you will be unable to make progress in developing your private and professional life.

The following examples illustrate this and show how positive thinking will increase your chances of success.

Private Life

Example of a Trigger Situation

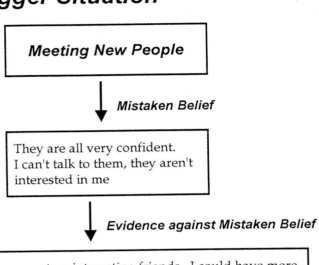

	Meeting New People

↓ *Mistaken Belief*

They are all very confident.
I can't talk to them, they aren't interested in me

↓ *Evidence against Mistaken Belief*

I already have one or two interesting friends. I could have more if I made the effort to contact people from time to time. I know that other people who appear confident inside really feel the same as I do.

Negative Thinking (ignores evidence – refuses to look at positive facts)

Positive Thinking (accepts evidence and acts on it)

I find it too hard.
I can't make small talk
I've nothing interesting to offer; people will think I'm dull or stupid

There is no reason why people shouldn't like me. Nothing stands between me and other people unless I hold myself back

↓ *Negative Behaviour*

↓ *Positive Behaviour*

Poor eye contact
Negative body language
Withdrawn behaviour
Unwillingness to be drawn into conversation
Looks disinterested

Good eye contact
Positive body language
Makes effort to engage other people in conversation
Looks interested

↓ *Negative Results*

↓ *Positive Results*

Meeting new people becomes more and more difficult. Social and conversational skills diminish leading to fewer social activities and loneliness.

You become more outgoing in social situations and develop conversational skills which leads to more fulfilling social life and increased circle of friends.

Negative Thinking Produces Negative Results

Positive Thinking Produces Positive Results

Professional Life

Example of a Trigger Situation

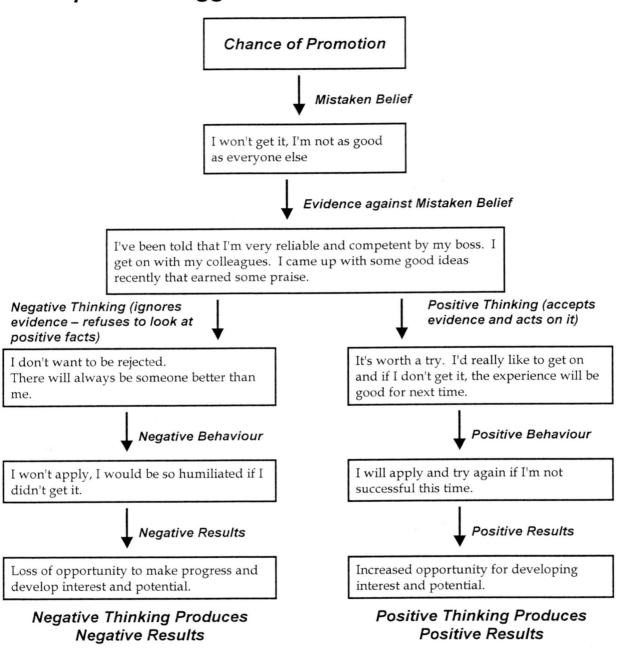

Chance of Promotion

↓ *Mistaken Belief*

I won't get it, I'm not as good as everyone else

↓ *Evidence against Mistaken Belief*

I've been told that I'm very reliable and competent by my boss. I get on with my colleagues. I came up with some good ideas recently that earned some praise.

Negative Thinking (ignores evidence – refuses to look at positive facts)

Positive Thinking (accepts evidence and acts on it)

I don't want to be rejected. There will always be someone better than me.

It's worth a try. I'd really like to get on and if I don't get it, the experience will be good for next time.

↓ *Negative Behaviour*

↓ *Positive Behaviour*

I won't apply, I would be so humiliated if I didn't get it.

I will apply and try again if I'm not successful this time.

↓ *Negative Results*

↓ *Positive Results*

Loss of opportunity to make progress and develop interest and potential.

Increased opportunity for developing interest and potential.

Negative Thinking Produces Negative Results

Positive Thinking Produces Positive Results

Private Life

Use the same situation to fill in the boxes as in the example model

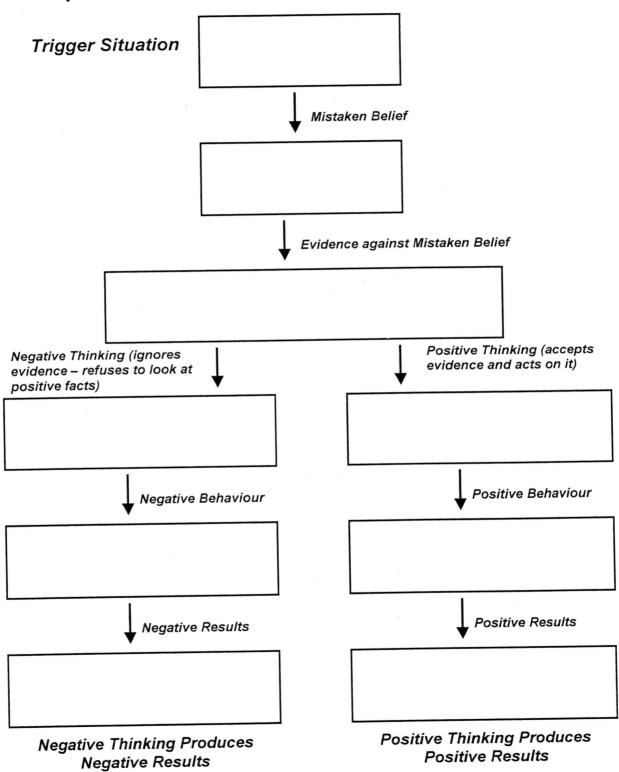

Trigger Situation

Mistaken Belief

Evidence against Mistaken Belief

Negative Thinking (ignores evidence – refuses to look at positive facts)

Positive Thinking (accepts evidence and acts on it)

Negative Behaviour

Positive Behaviour

Negative Results

Positive Results

Negative Thinking Produces Negative Results

Positive Thinking Produces Positive Results

Professional Life

Use the same situation to fill in the boxes as in the example model

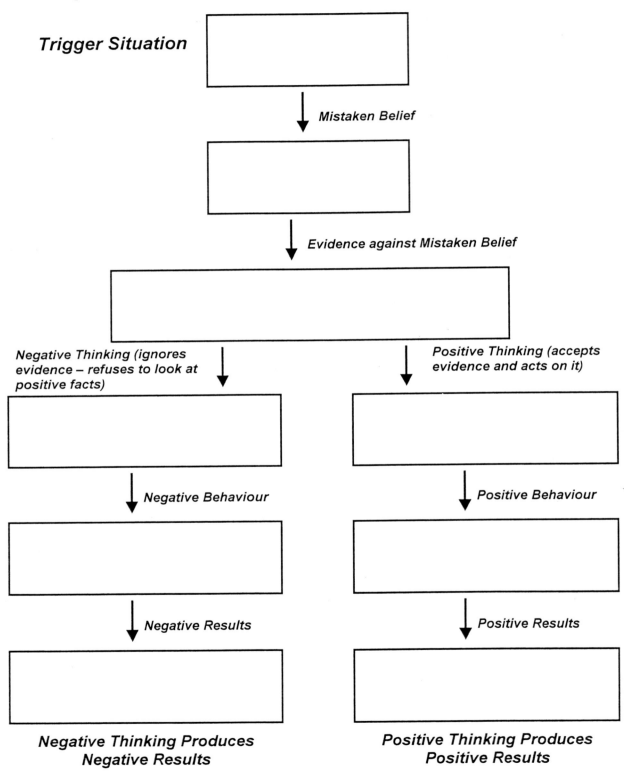

Trigger Situation

↓ *Mistaken Belief*

↓ *Evidence against Mistaken Belief*

Negative Thinking (ignores evidence – refuses to look at positive facts)

Positive Thinking (accepts evidence and acts on it)

↓ *Negative Behaviour*

↓ *Positive Behaviour*

↓ *Negative Results*

↓ *Positive Results*

Negative Thinking Produces Negative Results

Positive Thinking Produces Positive Results

Challenging your Negative Beliefs

From the previous exercises you will realise that you do have a choice in how you respond to key events or situations. The following exercise demonstrates even more clearly how the choice is now yours.

If you find yourself often saying these things to yourself then these beliefs will keep you within a Negative Cycle in your Private and Professional Life.

I've never been any good at ... !

I need lots of approval to know I'm doing the right thing.

I've got to show that I'm capable all the time in order for people to like me or for me to like myself.

If things go wrong or I make a mistake then life is terrible and I'm completely miserable.

Nice people continuously do things for other people and put their needs first.

I must show I'm in control of my emotions, 'letting go' is a sign of weakness.

It's too late to change as I've always been like this.

It's important that I keep my life and others lives as easy and even as possible – if I changed it could disrupt everything too much and people won't like me.

If someone is negative towards me it must be my fault in some way.

Remember Positive Thinking Leads to Positive Results which Leads to Positive Self-Esteem

Study the previous page

Select one of the negative beliefs and trace where it came from in your upbringing

Identify some of the other influential comments that dominated your life

Resolve now not to let these negative self-beliefs carry on dominating your life

Challenge them by identifying the negative belief and applying positive thinking

Example of how to challenge your negative beliefs using positive thinking

Comment	Nice people continuously do things for other people and put their needs first.
Challenge	If I continuously do things for other people I'll get too exhausted and 'burn out'. The people I respect make some time for themselves. I've never liked martyrs. I can only 'give' to others once I've learnt to give to myself. My mother always told me this and look where it got her!

Select a comment from one of your own negative beliefs and challenge it

Comment	
Challenge	

An optimist is wrong just about as often as a pessimist is, but the big difference is that he has a lot more fun.

Anonymous

Develop Positive Beliefs

These will keep you within an Upward Cycle of Good Self-Esteem in your Private and Professional Life

I can't expect everyone to like me – after all, I don't like everyone I meet.

I have strengths to offer if I choose to.

I have achieved some positive things in my life and I will again.

I have a right to think differently and believe in different things from other people.

I have got all sorts of interesting ideas and experiences that I can share if I want to.

Making mistakes is OK – I can learn from these – and it allows others to as well.

I can understand and forgive other people who have hurt me; being 'adult' means that I can start to sort things out for myself; I don't have to go on blaming people.

Sometimes new experiences are very exciting.

I can't solve all the problems I'm confronted with – sometimes I might have to choose to live with them or remove them or myself from them!

I have dreams and hopes that make me special and unique.

I have had some good relationships in the past and I will have again in the future.

I am not an endless 'resource' for others; I must stock up on 'reserves' and not get too drained.

I have inner creative talents which have been hidden for a long time and need a chance to grow.

The 'perfect' parent, partner or child does not exist – the 'good enough' one does!

I do not have to have everyone's approval all the time to know that I'm trying my hardest.

Now select one that you need to believe in more strongly and write it down where you can see it every day – read it and believe it!

Believe in Your Positive Qualities

One of the findings of the 'Human Potentialities Research Project' in the U.S.A. (1969) has been that the average, healthy, well-functioning person has a very limited awareness of her own personality strengths and resources, but has a much clearer picture of her weaknesses and problem areas. In other words we all tend to focus on our faults rather than our positive qualities. It was also found that the process of encouraging people to make a list of their strengths and attributes brought gains in self-confidence and improved their self-esteem.

Therefore it is important that we, too, take time to assess all our skills and qualities and acknowledge all the positive things we achieve in our lives.

First say to yourself what you would be; and then do what you have to do.

Epictetus – Discourses.

What I like about myself

Now jot down positive responses to these statements on your own. Be as honest with yourself as possible.

My Private Self

Any relationship skill I have.	
Anything I achieved at home which took a great deal of effort.	
Any spare time activities or hobbies.	
Anything I do to help others.	
Any features of my personality that please me.	
Anyway in which I have recently changed.	
Anything I have written or said.	
Any achievement I am proud of.	
Any special talent I have.	

My Professional Self

Any colleague I work well with.	
Any project or piece of work I am proud of.	
Any new skill I have developed.	
Any idea or scheme I have contributed.	
Any difficult problem arising from my job I have solved.	
Any colleague I have helped.	
Any area where my aptitudes or skills have been particularly useful.	
Any appreciative comment from a colleague.	
Any praise or recognition from my boss.	
Any new challenge I have taken on.	

Write down the two statements from each section that are most important to you and that have added to your self-confidence.

| |
| |
| |

Write down the two things you would like to feel more confident about.

| |
| |
| |

Now think of ways which would help to boost your confidence in these two areas.

| |
| |

Write your answers in the boxes

How did you feel while you were filling this in?

Do you find it difficult to see the positive in yourself?

Do you find it difficult to say positive things about yourself to others? Or even to admit them to yourself? If so, why do you think this is?

Now select certain statements from your lists and write yourself a positive character reference for your private and professional lives

Positive Reference for My Private Life

Positive Reference for My Professional Life

Taking Action

Taking Action in your Private Life

Read through the boxes below and circle five areas in which you feel you have low self-esteem and where you would most like to see an improvement.

Relationship with partner	Relationship with other members of family	Meeting new people	Developing friendships
Travelling alone	Organising parties or 'gatherings'	Comparing yourself with other women	Developing your own talents or skills
Making time for yourself	Putting yourself down in front of other people	Pleasing other people	Discussing problems
Personal appearance	Learning new skills	Making changes in your life	Becoming involved in activities outside the home

Fill in some or all of the blank boxes with further areas in which you feel you have low self-esteem and where you would most like to see an improvement.

Private Life

An example of how to tackle an area of low self-esteem

```
┌─────────────────────────────────┐
│ Area of Low Self-Esteem         │
│                                 │
│ Travelling alone                │
└─────────────────────────────────┘
```

What I would most want to change?

Being nervous about driving any distance or anywhere unfamiliar.

What would help me?

More experience
Relaxation exercises

What might hinder me?

Finding excuses not to travel alone, being frightened of getting lost, worrying about punctures, accidents etc.

What first step should I take?

Travel to a friend's house some distance away with clear directions.

What is my long term goal?

To be able to travel abroad without fear or worry.

How will I achieve this?

Continue to build up distance and then travel to new places making sure I have adequate maps. I have checked my car, so that I will gradually get more confident. Practise relaxation exercises before and during journey. Reward myself with lots of positive self-talk.

Private Life

A further example of how to tackle an area of low self-esteem

> **Area of Low Self-Esteem**
>
> *Making time for yourself*

What would I most want to change?

> *Never having time to do what I want to do.*

What would help me?

> *If I didn't give in to the constant demands of my family and friends.*

What might hinder me?

> *Feeling guilty. Constantly repeating a pattern of fitting in with other people. Their expectations that I will always be the same.*

What first step should I take?

> *Make one evening special for myself. Tell everyone I am unavailable and buy myself some special body luxuries, some exotic fruit and a good book, or hire a video of a film I have always wanted to see.*

What is my long term goal?

> *To have set aside a special time each week to 'do my own thing'.*

How will I achieve this?

> *Talk to my family and get their co-operation. Plan a time each week; be ruthless in keeping that time for myself.*

Private Life

A further example

> **Area of Low Self-Esteem**
>
> *Comparing yourself with other women*

What would I most want to change?

Feeling that most other women are better than me.

What would help me?

To develop more confidence in myself.

What might hinder me?

Negative thinking about myself.

What first step should I take?

Take time to think more about my good points and write them down. Ask a valued friend or member of my family to contribute to the list.

What is my long term goal?

To value my own strengths and realise that I am as worthwhile as anyone else.

How will I achieve this?

Positive thinking
Spending more time on myself
Joining an evening class and learning a new skill
Asking other people for positive feedback

All that we are is the result of what we have thought.

Buddha

Private Life

Now look at your five chosen areas of low self-esteem, select one and tackle it in the same way as the previous examples

> **Area of Low Self-Esteem**

What would I most want to change?

What would help me?

What might hinder me?

What first step should I take?

What is my long term goal?

How will I achieve this?

Private Life

Check list to help you maintain good self-esteem:

Write down a positive statement in each box.

Think and talk in a positive way about yourself *Examples* *I am good at painting* *I enjoy visiting the theatre/live bands etc.* *I am happy when I spend time with my friends.* *I look stunning in this outfit* *I am going to organise a dinner party on Saturday*	In future one of the positive things I will say about myself is ....

Avoid negative thoughts and self-talk *Examples* *I am so depressed* *I am really stupid* *I'll never be able to do that* *I'm too nervous to invite her for a coffee* *I wish I was slimmer/taller/prettier*	In future one of the negative thoughts I will avoid is ...

Private Life

Be comfortable with your appearance	In future I am going to ...
Wear clothes that help you to feel relaxed. Choose styles that reflect different aspects of your personality. Try out new images. Learn to smile and present a warm and friendly image. Look relaxed and project welcoming body language.	

Improve your social skills	In future I will ...
Watch the news and keep up-to-date with world events. Choose one or two subjects you are interested in and read more about them. Learn and practise ways of starting conversations. Follow up interesting new contacts with a phone call and perhaps an invitation for coffee. Keep your mind active by reading and studying. Don't just sit in front of a TV. Be selective about your programmes.	

Private Life

Create new experiences	In future I am going to ...
See new challenges as opportunities to widen your experience of life. Boost your confidence by learning a new skill or developing an existing talent in your life. Consider joining a new organisation. Consider having a completely different hobby. Travel somewhere completely new. Have an activity weekend break in a different setting.	

Relationships	In future I need to spend more time ...
Take time to evaluate your relationships. Have the courage to discard unhappy relationships. If necessary seek counselling help. Don't just stick to 'safe' relationships – increase your circle of friends; join different clubs or associations. Assess your own needs within relationships and make sure they are being met. Make sure your relationships are based on mutual affection, trust, care, and respect. Tell people close to you that you love them and show signs and gestures of affection.	

Positive versus Negative	In future I will spend more time ...
Concentrate on friends/acquaintances with whom you can enjoy interesting, stimulating talks.	
Avoid friends/acquaintances with whom you always moan about the negative areas in your life.	
Remember and think about all the supportive and encouraging statements people have made about you.	
Don't dwell on negative comments people have made about you.	
Carry on listing your strengths and make sure they are being put to good use.	**In future I will spend less time ...**
Don't allow your areas of weakness to overcome you.	
When you make a mistake value the experience as a useful learning exercise.	
Don't allow mistakes to become total failures.	

Remember Positive Thinking Leads to Positive Results which Leads to Positive Self-Esteem

Professional Life

Taking action in your Professional Life

Read through the boxes below and circle five areas you feel lower your self-esteem and which you would most like to see an improvement. Add any to the empty boxes.

Relationship with boss	Relationship with colleagues	Suitability of work (physically)	Suitability of work (intellectually)
Suitability of hours	Self-presentation	Organisational skills	Appraisal of work
Opportunity for promotion	Opportunity for change/variety	Level of responsibility	Opportunity to delegate
Opportunity for input of personal ideas/projects	Discussing problems	Learning new skills	Competitiveness amongst colleagues
Competence at work	Punctuality at work	Opportunity for social time with colleagues	

Professional Life

> **Area of Low Self-Esteem**
>
> *My inability to discuss work problems*

What would I most want to change?

> *I never talk about problems at work with colleagues. I keep them to myself and feel resentful.*

What would help me?

> *Positive thinking, i.e. believing my views are as important and valid as anyone else's.*

What might hinder me?

> *Fear of being 'put down' or my view being totally ignored.*

What first step should I take?

> *Clarify in my mind exactly what is my problem, what do I feel about it, and what do I need.*
>
> *Be brave and tackle minor problems with the colleague I feel closest to.*

What is my long term goal?

> *To be able to 'iron out' all the problems that arise in my work life. To be open and able to communicate well.*

How will I achieve this?

> *I will learn how to be assertive and how to negotiate.*
>
> *I will take time to reflect on problems; write down the problem and first see if I can sort it out.*
>
> *I will learn to listen well to other people's problems so that they view me as someone worth spending time with.*

Professional Life

An example of how to tackle an area of low self-esteem

Area of Low Self-Esteem
My organisational skill

What would I most want to change?

> *I don't have the confidence to organise the agenda for one of our staff meetings.*

What would help me?

> *Believing I could do it successfully. Realising that other people feel the same as me and that I could do an equally good, if not better, job if I really tried.*

> *To stop using negative thinking, i.e. thinking I would make a total mess of it all. Making silly excuses to myself, e.g. that I haven't got the time to research the necessary topics.*

What first step should I take?

> *Prepare a 'mock' meeting and enlist the help of my friends to role-play the meeting in the safety of my own home.*

What is my long term goal?

> *To be able to organise these meetings as efficiently as colleagues without panicking and feeling inadequate.*

How will I achieve this?

> *Read around the subject.*

> *Perfect the skills I need with friends' help.*

> *Go to local college to find out what courses are available on self-presentation, communication skills etc.*

> *Make sure I research my chosen topic thoroughly and leave plenty of time to prepare the agenda.*

> *Learn and practise relaxation exercises.*

Professional Life

A further example of how to take an area of low self-esteem

> **Area of Low Self-Esteem**
>
> *My attitude to learning new skills*

What would I most want to change?

> *I'd really like to add to the skills I possess, but I don't think I'm important enough for the company to pay for me to attend a course or to allow me the time off to do it.*

What would help me?

> *Believing I am as deserving as other colleagues who have learnt new skills.*
>
> *Believing that I have a lot to offer to the organisation especially if I developed certain areas of expertise.*
>
> *To stop using negative thinking, e.g. fear of rejection, not believing in my rights.*

What first step should I take?

> *Read up about all the courses in my area of work and select one I feel I most need at the present time.*

What is my long term goal?

> *To learn new skills to make me better qualified and able to seek promotion.*

How will I achieve this?

> *Decide exactly which course/courses I would like to do. Make a list of all the benefits to the company, which would arise from my new skill. Have a clear plan of where I want to go in my career, practise 'asking the boss' with friends who could give me constructive advice.*
>
> *Ask the boss.*

Professional Life

Now look at your five chosen areas of low self-esteem, select one and tackle it in the same way as the previous examples

> **Area of Low Self-Esteem**

What would I most want to change?

What would help me?

What might hinder me?

What first small step should I take?

What is my long term goal?

How will I achieve this?

Professional Life

Check list to help you maintain good self-esteem:

Write down a positive statement in each box.

Assess your career	In future I am going to change ...
Do you enjoy what you are doing? Evaluate your attitude to your work and assess how fulfilling it is - perhaps you need a change of career or even to change direction.	
Are you happy about your personal contribution or is something holding you back?	
Increase your motivation with a new challenge or more responsibility.	
Think positively about your future; decide and write down where you want to be in five years time.	

Consider promotion	In future I will ...
Have confidence in your abilities and believe that not only are you good enough for promotion, you owe it to yourself to develop your potential.	
Show the boss and colleagues that you care about the company's interests.	
Make sure that all your effort is noted, i.e. be seen to be good at your job and don't be over modest about your achievements.	
Talk about your successes and report on them.	
Show yourself willing to help out at crisis times.	
Seek professional advice if you are unsure of which direction you should take, e.g. make an appointment with the personnel officer.	

Professional Life

Developing your work skills	In future I will definitely ...
Keep up-to-date with what is happening in your area of work, e.g. read books, subscribe to a work-related journal.	
Don't get left behind through neglecting to embrace modern technology.	
Be ready and willing to attend courses and seminars.	
Consider initiating new schemes or projects to keep your organisation competitive.	
Consider writing up any new initiatives you have been involved in for a relevant work journal or magazine.	

Self-presentation and motivation	In future I am going to ...
Does your personal appearance reflect the image you wish to promote? (e.g. calm and capable, exciting and energetic)	
Make any changes to your appearance if you feel it would boost your confidence, seek advice if necessary.	
Be positive in what you say at work; no-one likes a constant moaner or someone who does not pull their weight.	
Increase your energy by taking up a physical sport.	

Professional Life

Positive feedback	In future I need to...
Set yourself short term goals at work, e.g. updating your files, emptying your in-tray once a week, making time to have an important conversation with a colleague, and reward yourself when you achieve your goal with a 'special treat'.	
Ask your boss for regular appraisals of your work, so that you can monitor your progress and enjoy your success, and work on your weaknesses.	
Keep a daily diary noting down everyday achievements.	
Create further opportunities for success.	

Colleagues	In future I am going to make sure that I ...
Create mutual respect and trust between yourself and your colleagues by building their self-esteem. Give regular genuine praise and encouragement.	
Attend any business/work functions and make some time to get to know colleagues.	
Avoid undue criticism, 'put-downs' or back-stabbing!	
Be supportive and helpful to colleagues.	
Project a welcoming and friendly image.	
Give good quality listening time to colleagues.	
Make sure you communicate properly with people - don't hog the information.	

Professional Life

Positive versus Negative	In future I will do more ...
Always think of ways to keep your career interesting and enjoyable.	
Don't stick in a dull and unfulfilling job because it is safe or you can't think of anything else to do.	
Concentrate on positive thinking to help you make progress and enjoy success.	
Don't allow the way you view mistakes or set-backs to affect the way you view your career. You can learn from them and try again.	In future I will do less ...
Believe in your abilities and your values as an important member of your workforce.	
Don't put yourself down and think that all your colleagues have more to offer.	

Remember Positive Thinking Leads to Positive Results which Leads to Positive Self-Esteem

2

Dealing with Stress in your Private and Professional Life

Dealing with Stress

Introduction

Stress is a natural condition and part of your life. Some of the stressful aspects of your life are caused by living in a fast-moving society, others are caused by your own perceptions of a situation and the way in which you react. The way you cope with stress enhances or lowers your self-esteem. The important issue in determining our well-being is how we cope with stress and whether the strategies we adopt are positive and successful or negative and therefore likely to prolong the stress. This section looks at both types of response and how this can affect your private and professional life.

What is Stress?

Stress is a natural condition and a necessary means of survival. It produces the vital physical changes needed to make bodies work faster and harder when they are faced with physically or emotionally threatening situations.

If you are crossing a road and notice a car coming rapidly towards you, it is your anxiety which helps you jump out of the way. A 'threat' is recognised by one of your senses, i.e. eyes, ears, nose, and the message sent to your brain (see diagram below).

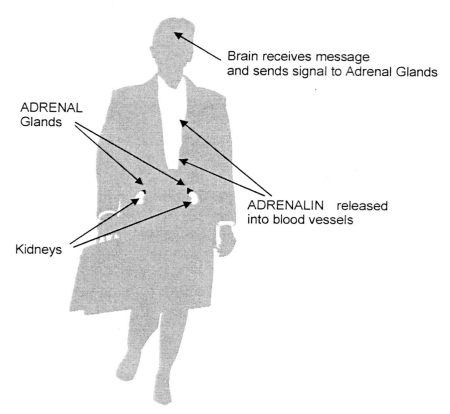

Brain receives message
and sends signal to Adrenal Glands

ADRENAL
Glands

ADRENALIN released
into blood vessels

Kidneys

In exactly the same way, if someone makes a sharp critical remark to you it is your anxiety which can make your muscles tense or your heart beat faster. In both cases, if a person feels physically or emotionally threatened, their body takes some action to prepare them to run away or to confront the situation. The brain sends a message to the adrenal glands, situated above your kidneys, to release adrenaline into your bloodstream in order that your body can either go into 'fight' or 'flight', i.e. either confront or avoid the stressful situation.

Stress produces physical changes in your body. The adrenaline which the adrenal glands release is passed around your body in the bloodstream. When it reaches your heart, lungs muscles, etc. it makes changes to help you fight or run away

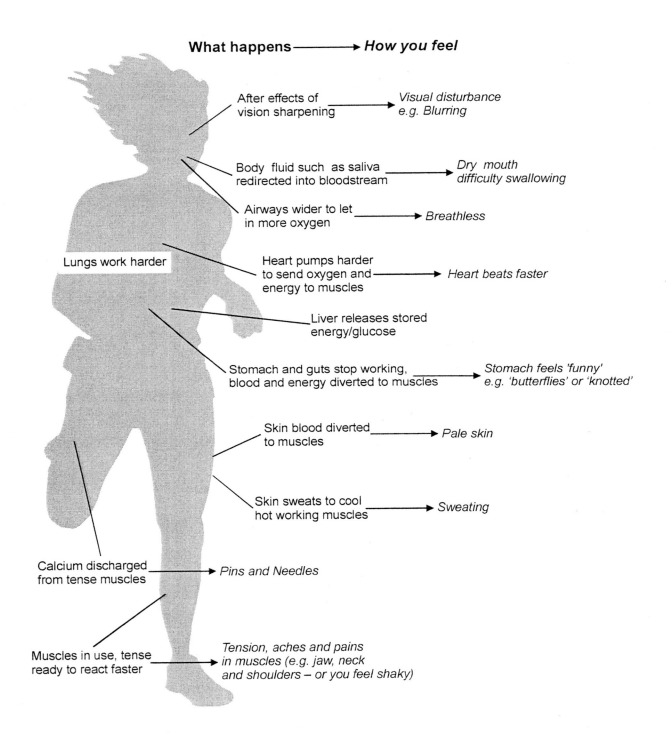

What happens ——→ How you feel

After effects of vision sharpening ——→ *Visual disturbance e.g. Blurring*

Body fluid such as saliva redirected into bloodstream ——→ *Dry mouth difficulty swallowing*

Airways wider to let in more oxygen ——→ *Breathless*

Lungs work harder

Heart pumps harder to send oxygen and energy to muscles ——→ *Heart beats faster*

Liver releases stored energy/glucose

Stomach and guts stop working, blood and energy diverted to muscles ——→ *Stomach feels 'funny' e.g. 'butterflies' or 'knotted'*

Skin blood diverted to muscles ——→ *Pale skin*

Skin sweats to cool hot working muscles ——→ *Sweating*

Calcium discharged from tense muscles ——→ *Pins and Needles*

Muscles in use, tense ready to react faster ——→ *Tension, aches and pains in muscles (e.g. jaw, neck and shoulders – or you feel shaky)*

From the diagram you can see the number of physical changes that occur in the body when it is presented with a threatening situation, in order to help you 'fight' the danger or 'flee' from it.

An emotional threat to our self-esteem will produce the same physical changes within our bodies. The tension we then feel can only be reduced by 'fight' – facing up to the confrontation, or 'flight' – running away and avoiding the confrontation. If neither option is possible we remain feeling stressed until the adrenalin in our bodies is used up, which can be a considerable time, especially if we think negatively about ourselves or put ourselves down.

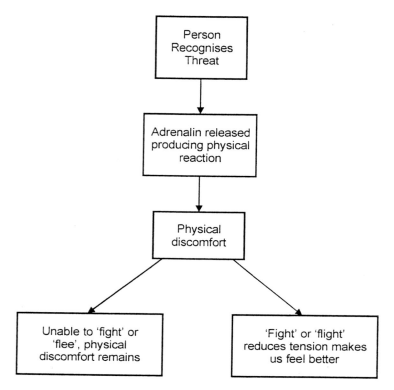

When we feel stressed we tend to adopt negative thinking and to say things like:

> "This is terrible, I feel awful"
> "I'll never overcome my shyness"
> "Everyone thinks I'm, stupid"
> "I hate being here, I wish I could leave"

These negative thoughts are unhelpful because they make us feel more frightened which stimulates the body to produce more adrenalin, thereby increasing our physical discomfort (e.g. tongue-tied, blushing, panic attack).

Understanding Stress in your Private and Professional Life

This chart estimates the levels of stress induced by the various life events we face. People who have to cope with too many stressful factors at once are more at risk of suffering from health problems.

	Life Event Scores (adapted from Holmes & Rahe 1987)	
Death of someone close to you	100	
Divorce	73	
Separation	65	
Death of close member of family	63	
Illness or injury	53	
Marriage	50	
Termination of employment	47	
Reconciliation with spouse	45	
Retirement	45	
Illness in family	45	
Pregnancy	40	
Sexual problems	39	
New family member	39	
Change of work	39	
Financial change	38	
Death of friend	37	
Change of employment	36	
Increasing mortgage	31	
Child leaving home	29	
Conflict with in-laws	29	
Outstanding achievement	28	
Child starting/leaving school	26	
Change of social activities	25	
Conflict with boss	23	
Change of social activities	18	
Change in sleep pattern	16	
Change in eating habits	15	
Holiday	13	
Christmas	12	
	Your total	

Thomas Holmes and Richard Rahe researched the effect of different events on people's health. Their findings showed that for people who had a life event score below 100 there was a 1 in 100 chance of them becoming ill during the next year. The risk increased with the life event score i.e.

Score	Risk of Illness
100 – 149	3 in 10
150 – 299	5 in 10
300 +	8 in 10

The table was intended to study groups of people and therefore does not take into account individual differences, but it does serve as an indication of how events in our lives can affect our health and well-being.

Understanding your Stress Profile

What type of person are you? Tick the statements in each box that apply to you

Type A

Very competitive	
Ambitious socially/at work	
Punctual	
Strong, forceful personality	
Impatient	
Walks, moves and eats quickly	
Likes to do several tasks at once	
Easily angered by events or people	
Seeks public recognition	
Has trouble relaxing	
Always rushed	
Few interests outside home/work	
Hides feelings	
Pushes self/others to get things done	

Type B

Not competitive	
Happy with present social/work position	
Casual about time-keeping	
Easy going personality	
Patient	
Walks, moves and eats without rushing	
Concentrates on one task at a time	
Slow to anger	
Not interested in public recognition	
Enjoys periods of relaxation	
Never feels rushed	
Has interests outside home/work	
Is able to show feelings	
Doesn't push self/others to get things done	

Count up how many statements you have ticked in each box and decide whether you are more a type 'A' or type 'B' personality.

If you are a Type A personality you are more likely to suffer from some of the adverse effects of stress, i.e. feelings of tension, headaches or illness. Furthermore you might find that you experience problems with your inter-personal relationships and often feel discontented with your life. Type B personalities tend to enjoy better health and experience more satisfaction in their lives, although there can be a tendency for these types to be too 'laid back' and lacking in motivation.

If you are more of a Type A personality you might recognise some of the stress responses that are shown on the following two pages. Make a mental note of how many of these apply to you.

Physical Responses to Stress

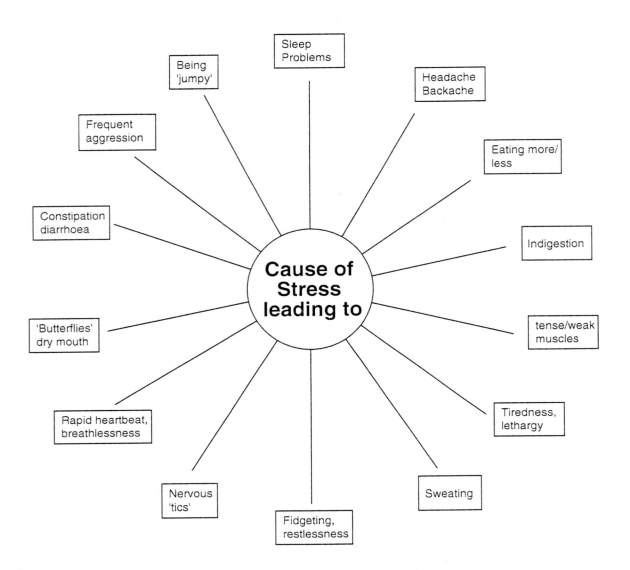

How many of these do you experience?

Emotional and Intellectual Responses to Stress

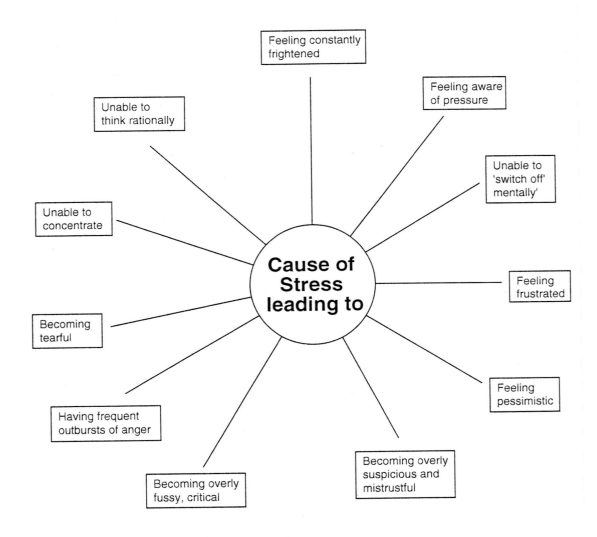

Feeling constantly frightened

Feeling aware of pressure

Unable to think rationally

Unable to 'switch off' mentally'

Unable to concentrate

Cause of Stress leading to

Feeling frustrated

Becoming tearful

Feeling pessimistic

Having frequent outbursts of anger

Becoming overly suspicious and mistrustful

Becoming overly fussy, critical

How many of these do you experience?

Private Life

How well are you coping with stress?

Look at the list below and circle a number in the scale beside each item to indicate how frequently the item causes you anxiety, i.e. ① never causes you anxiety, ④ sometimes causes you anxiety, ⑦ always causes you anxiety.

Your husband/partner	1	2	3	4	5	6	7
Children	1	2	3	4	5	6	7
Shopping	1	2	3	4	5	6	7
Preparing meal	1	2	3	4	5	6	7
Housework	1	2	3	4	5	6	7
Visiting relatives	1	2	3	4	5	6	7
Selecting your clothes	1	2	3	4	5	6	7
Health	1	2	3	4	5	6	7
Spiritual self	1	2	3	4	5	6	7
Sleep pattern	1	2	3	4	5	6	7
Time alone	1	2	3	4	5	6	7
Hobbies	1	2	3	4	5	6	7
Decorating	1	2	3	4	5	6	7
Social Life	1	2	3	4	5	6	7
Friendships	1	2	3	4	5	6	7
Finances	1	2	3	4	5	6	7
Holidays	1	2	3	4	5	6	7
Car Problems	1	2	3	4	5	6	7
Gardening	1	2	3	4	5	6	7
Neighbours	1	2	3	4	5	6	7

Add together all the numbers you have circled and write down your total score

Total Score

Well done! You are coping well with all the stress factors in your life. Just make sure that you are looking after yourself and giving yourself sufficient treats.	*Despite all the stresses that are affecting you, you are managing to keep things in perspective. Some things seem to be out of your control and you do need to learn positive coping responses for specific areas in your life.*	*Things really get on top of you. Life must feel like an upward battle with little time for relaxation and peace of mind. Your coping responses are negative and ineffective. You deserve better from life and must start to take stress management more seriously before your emotional and physical health deteriorates.*
20 – 60	*61 – 100*	*101 – 140*

Professional Life

How are well you coping with stress?

Look at the list below and circle a number in the scale beside each item to indicate how frequently the item causes you anxiety, i.e. ① never causes you anxiety, ④ sometimes causes you anxiety, ⑦ always causes you anxiety.

Physical surroundings	1	2	3	4	5	6	7
Contact with boss	1	2	3	4	5	6	7
Contact with colleagues	1	2	3	4	5	6	7
Overlong working hours	1	2	3	4	5	6	7
Meeting deadlines	1	2	3	4	5	6	7
Using technology/equipment	1	2	3	4	5	6	7
Work encroaching on personal time (e.g. lunchbreaks, evening, weekends)	1	2	3	4	5	6	7
Sexual harassment	1	2	3	4	5	6	7
Undefined objectives	1	2	3	4	5	6	7
Poor instructions	1	2	3	4	5	6	7
Making decisions	1	2	3	4	5	6	7
Poor eating/drinking habits	1	2	3	4	5	6	7
Sexual/racial discrimination	1	2	3	4	5	6	7
Taking on extra work (e.g. through colleagues absence)	1	2	3	4	5	6	7
Punctuality	1	2	3	4	5	6	7
Lack of interest	1	2	3	4	5	6	7
Support from management	1	2	3	4	5	6	7
Promotion	1	2	3	4	5	6	7
Fitting in your holiday	1	2	3	4	5	6	7
Company performance	1	2	3	4	5	6	7

Add together all the numbers you have circled and write down your total score

Total Score

Great! You are managing to cope very well at work. Your ability to deal with stress is good. Are you sure, however, that you are meeting new challenges and have important goals to reach. You have great potential, make sure that you use it fully.	*Despite the stress that you have to cope with at work you are managing to do a good job. Occasionally, however, you do let things get on top of you. Because you do not manage these situations as well, you are not doing yourself justice or presenting yourself as successfully as you could.*	*Things are obviously affecting you far too much. Are you sure you are in the right job? If you think you are, then you must concentrate on developing your positive stress responses in order to have any career satisfaction.*
20 – 60	**61 – 100**	**101 – 140**

Developing Positive Responses to Stress

When we experience a stressful situation in our lives we make adjustments in our behaviour and thinking in order to cope. However, sometimes the responses we make are inappropriate or inadequate and do not deal effectively with the cause of stress. These are negative coping responses and can even increase the level of stress that we are experiencing. When confronted by a cause of stress we have a choice as to whether we adopt positive or negative coping responses. The following model illustrates the choices we make.

Example in Private Life

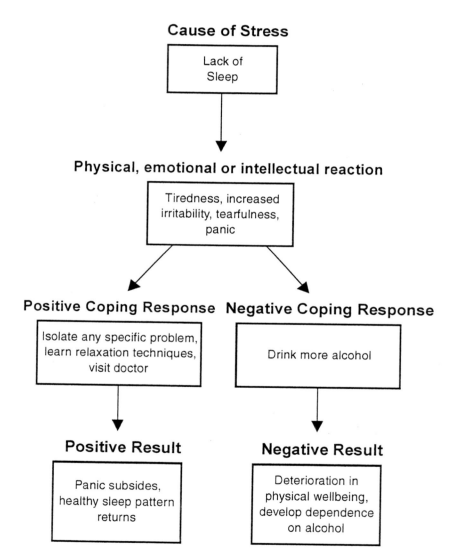

Cause of Stress

Lack of Sleep

Physical, emotional or intellectual reaction

Tiredness, increased irritability, tearfulness, panic

Positive Coping Response

Isolate any specific problem, learn relaxation techniques, visit doctor

Negative Coping Response

Drink more alcohol

Positive Result

Panic subsides, healthy sleep pattern returns

Negative Result

Deterioration in physical wellbeing, develop dependence on alcohol

Positive thinking leads to positive coping strategies
Negative thinking leads to negative coping strategies

Example in Professional Life

Cause of Stress

```
Sexual
harrassment
at work
```

Physical, emotional or intellectual reaction

```
Feelings of frustration,
anger, fear of being alone
at work, being 'jumpy'
```

Positive Coping Response **Negative Coping Response**

```
Talk through problems
with a trusted person
Confront offender in a
calm way. Still offending?
Seek professional advice
```

```
Grumbling to colleagues,
sarcastic remarks
to 'offender'
```

Positive Result **Negative Result**

```
Professional advice
enables you to
remove problem
```

```
Depression or anxiety attacks
develop about going to and
being at work
```

Private Life

Now fill in the boxes below, as in the previous example models, using a situation from your own private life which causes you stress.

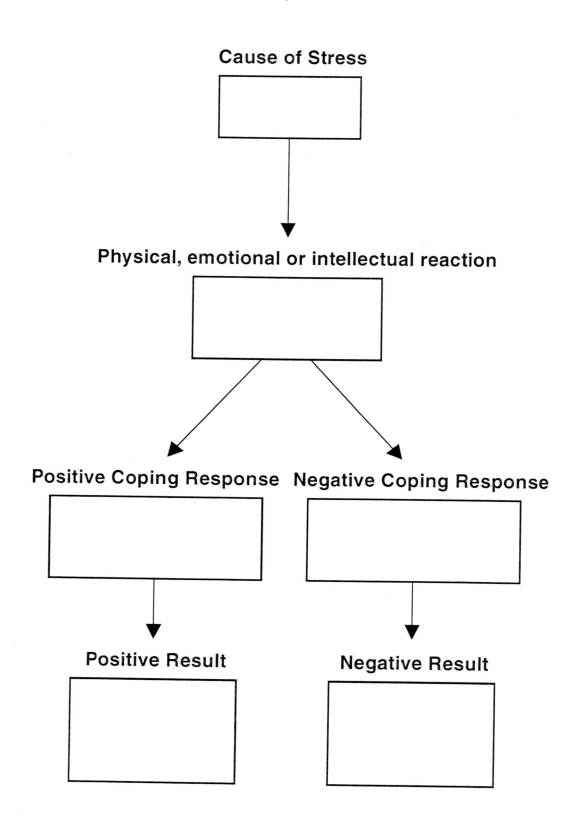

Professional Life

Now fill in the boxes below, as in the example model, using a situation from your own professional life which causes you stress.

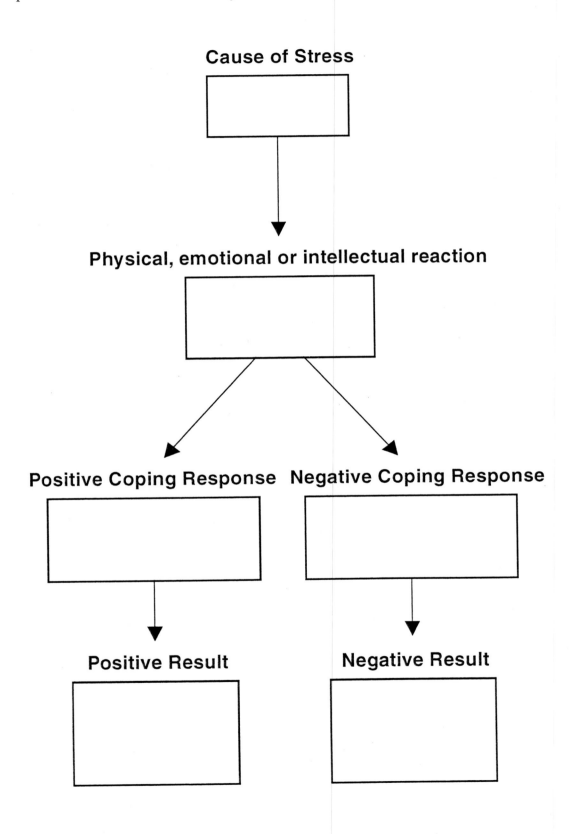

Cause of Stress

Physical, emotional or intellectual reaction

Positive Coping Response **Negative Coping Response**

Positive Result **Negative Result**

Private Life

A case study to show the effects of negative coping responses to stress

Jane is awakened three times during the night by her baby son who is teething. At 8.15 am she awakes with a start realising that she has overslept and immediately wakes her husband Mike. He is annoyed with her, as he particularly wanted to arrive at his workplace early to prepare notes for a meeting with his immediate superior at 9.30 am. Jane retaliates angrily, "Perhaps if you ever bothered to get up and see to the baby occasionally, I might not be so tired and oversleep". More angry exchanges pass between them.

Jane wakes her older child and nags her to get dressed and ready for school. Breakfast time is rushed and tense; Mike fumes silently while he is waiting for his child to be ready to leave. When they are ready, the two of them rush out of the door without saying goodbye to Jane. "They think I'm some sort of automaton", she mutters to herself as she hears the baby cry.

The baby refuses breakfast and is fretful. While she is dressing him he continues to cry and fights her attempts to clothe him. Jane shouts at the baby, which upsets him even more, then she bursts into tears.

Having at last composed herself and the baby, she hurriedly dresses, not bothering to put make-up on, and decides to placate the baby by taking him for a walk. As she pushes the baby to the local shop she meets a friend, who is immaculately groomed and on her way to a meeting. "You look dreadful!" the friend says, "Are you all right?"

"Yes fine", Jane mutters, noticing the porridge stain on her blouse. "Must rush, lots to do". "Stuck up cow", Jane thinks, noticing her dishevelled appearance in the shop window: "I could look like that if I was as selfish as her".

Having purchased the few items she needs, Jane decides to take the baby to the park, but on the way it begins to rain, so she returns home.

Her heart sinks when she opens the door and sees the dirty breakfast crockery and assorted litter lying around. She puts the baby down with a biscuit and prepares to clear up, but the baby immediately cries and wants to be cuddled.

An hour later, having exhausted her stock of nursery rhymes and games, the baby falls asleep.

Jane decides to clear up quickly and then sit down and relax for a while with a good book. She has just made herself a coffee when the doorbell rings. "Damn", she thinks, "who the hell is that?" Her mother is on the doorstep. "Oh good, I'm glad you're in, I want you to help me write a letter to my solicitor".

Jane helps her mother, but is not able to fully concentrate. "You're overtired", her mother says. "You should go to bed earlier".

"Why don't you buzz off and mind your own business", Jane thinks.

As her mother leaves, Jane becomes aware that the baby is now awake and crying once more.

In the afternoon Jane remembers she had said she would wash her husband's track suit, as he is playing football that evening. She puts the suit into the washing machine, then discovers she has no washing powder. She must walk to the shop again and it is raining heavily. She thinks angrily of Mike: "I'd like to see him manage to do his job and look after a baby".

The older child returns from school tired and hungry. She whines continuously. Jane locks herself in the toilet for 15 minutes to get some peace because she can feel her anger mounting and knows that she will begin to shout.

"God, I'm such a lousy mother", she thinks, "I never have any patience with them".

She struggles through the remainder of the afternoon feeding her daughter and getting the baby ready for bed. Her husband returns late from work. Jane thinks he has done this deliberately so as to avoid helping her with the children. "I expect your dinner is spoiled", she tells him, hoping that it is. She stubbornly refuses to ask how his meeting went.

At 9.00 pm, when all the chores are completed and the children in bed, Jane feels a twinge of guilt because she has been 'offish' with Mike. She decides to sit down and spend some time with him.

"I've had such a lousy day", she begins "so much pressure!"

"Pressure!" Mike expostulates, "You don't know what pressure is, you should have my job - work deadlines, meetings, bosses. God, you women lead the 'life of Riley'."

Jane leaps up and rushes out of the room, slamming the door. She goes to bed, but cannot get to sleep for some time as she is so tense. She has just managed to drop off when the baby's crying wakes her.

Private Life

Make a list of all the negative emotions and negative coping strategies experienced by Jane. Then suggest some positive coping strategies that she might have used instead and the positive emotions she might feel.

Negative Coping Response	Negative Emotion	Positive Coping Response	Positive Emotion
Example *Jane snaps at her husband when he wakes up and is annoyed at being late.*	*Anger, guilt, resentment*	*Jane explains she has overslept because she has had a disturbed night.*	*No guilt, pleased that she has calmed the situation*

Professional Life

A case study to show the effects of negative coping responses to stress

Sarah has overslept and is late (the third time this week) for work. She tries to sneak past her boss's office, but just at that moment he opens his door and, seeing her, looks at his watch. "I'm sorry I'm late", Sarah blurts out, "The car in front of me was involved in an accident", she lies, "and it held me up".

"This isn't the first time you've been late this week", her boss says, "and in fact your punctuality seems to have deteriorated considerably over the last few weeks". "I am overtired at the moment", Sarah replies, "but that's because I'm having to do all Alice's work as well as my own. She didn't finish her assignment before going on holiday, so I've had to do it in order to meet her deadline". This is a gross exaggeration, as Sarah had herself offered to complete just one page for her friend Alice, so that she could leave work promptly to go on holiday. Apart from this the assignment had been up to date and ready.

"Hmm", says her boss, "Well please try to arrive on time in future".

Sarah walks to her desk hoping that he doesn't mention this to Alice on Monday when she returns to work. Sarah is tired, she chain smokes and drinks endless cups of coffee throughout the morning in an attempt to stay alert.

During the morning she goes up to ask her head of department if he has any work for her. He has the reputation of office playboy and, smacking Sarah's behind, he asks: "How's my favourite girl today?" Smiling and acquiescent, she allows him to put his arm around her waist while he explains what work he wants her to do. Outside the office afterwards she thinks, "Dirty-minded old lecher", and resolves to 'lose' one of his letters, in the hope that he will get into trouble because of it. She feels compromised and 'dirty'.

At lunchtime Sarah realises that she has left her packed lunch at home, so has nothing to eat. She has a headache, but can't summon up the energy to go out for a walk in the fresh air. Instead she takes some painkillers with another cup of coffee, and smokes more cigarettes to quell her hunger pangs. A colleague, Chris, comes to chat to her. "I'm trying to get together a skittles team to play the crowd downstairs on Friday night, would you like to come along?" she asks. Sarah feels panicky. "Oh I'm sorry I can't", she replies, "I've already made other arrangements". This is not true, but she feels too shy to join work colleagues in social activities.

"Oh well, perhaps next time", says Chris.

"Yes, definitely", affirms Sarah, knowing very well that she won't.

By three in the afternoon Sarah is so hungry that she buys two bars of chocolate from the tea lady and eats them both.

She has trouble concentrating on her work and spends much time day-dreaming about meeting really exciting friends and having a wonderful social life. She imagines herself at a party being sought out by all sorts of interesting people because they admire her humour and intelligence. At 4.30 pm she realises with a sudden shock, how much time she has wasted on her day-dreams. She rushes to complete the letters in her in-tray, before the day ends. When they are finished she notices a typing error on one, but there is insufficient time to re-do it, so she decides to send it to the relevant person as it is; he can always send it back tomorrow, if he notices the mistake.

Sarah glances at the noticeboard, before she leaves. An opportunity for internal promotion is advertised. Sarah likes the sound of the new post, but thinks that Alice or Katy will probably apply and in which case she wouldn't stand a chance. "I won't bother to put my name forward", she decides.

Her boss sees her as she is leaving. "Come in a minute Sarah", he calls. When she is inside his office he tells her, "There's a three-day course next month which I think would be most beneficial to you. Here's the details, let me know after the weekend if you'd like to go".

Sarah thanks him, feeling sick already at the prospect of attending a course with strangers. As soon as she is outside of his office she begins to think of valid reasons why she can't go.

Sarah arrives home tired and deflated. She takes more painkillers for her throbbing headache and slumps in front of the television with a glass of wine. "I really hate my job", she tells her flat-mate, "it's so boring. The men are perverts or bullies and the women are creeps or stand-offish, and the work is tedious and uninteresting."

"Why don't you come out with me and some friends? Take your mind off it", suggests her flat-mate. "No thanks, I'm too tired", says Sarah.

Professional Life

Make a list of all the negative emotions and negative coping strategies experienced by Sarah. Then suggest some positive coping strategies that she might have used instead and the positive emotions she might feel.

Negative Coping Response	Negative Emotion	Positive Coping Response	Positive Emotion
Example *Lies to boss about lateness*	*Guilt, fear*	*Apologises and says she will try not to let it happen again.*	*Relief*

Coping Responses to Stress

Negative Responses	Positive Responses
Grumbling to others about a situation	Discuss problems with a safe and trusted person
Pretending a problem does not exist in the hope that it will go away.	Have the courage to tackle a difficult problem rather than ignoring it
Developing a psychosomatic illness	Acknowledge areas of weakness in yourself and resolve to take steps to do something about them
Shifting emotions from the actual target of stress onto a less threatening target	Seek professional help over problems
Finding 'valid' reasons to excuse your own or other people's behaviour	Join a support or self-help group
Becoming obsessive	Get negative feelings off your chest
Behaving in an inappropriate way	Learn relaxation techniques
Withdrawing into daydreaming and 'if only ...'	Take up a sport
Adopting a behaviour pattern which conflicts with your beliefs and values	Learn to say no to excessive demands on your time
Eating for comfort	Value your views and needs as much as other people's
Smoking, drinking alcohol or taking drugs	Find something to laugh at – humour is a great tonic
Blaming others for your inadequacies	Forgive yourself for any mistakes that you make – take time to learn from them
Rushing into situations that appear to offer immediate well-being	Consider different options in difficult or unresolved situations
Bursts of temper over unimportant things	Be willing to change
Feeling resentful that life has been unfair to you	Plan treats for yourself

Private Life

Find an area of stress in your life where you know you are using a negative coping response, think of an alternative positive coping response and then fill in the boxes.

Negative Coping Response	Positive Coping Response
Example: *Eating for comfort.*	*Face up to problem of why I eat for comfort. Join Weight Watchers, plan treats for successful weight loss.*
How this affects my life	**How I hope this will improve the situation**
Weight problems resulting in poor self-image.	*Remove need for comfort eating. Lose weight and be happier with my self-image.*

Professional Life

Find an area of stress in your work where you know you are using a negative coping strategy and think of an alternative positive coping strategy

Negative Coping Strategy	Positive Coping Strategy
Example: *Moaning to colleagues about workload.*	*Make appointment with boss to discuss problem.*
How this affects my life	**How I hope this will improve the situation**
I feel constantly resentful and don't enjoy work.	*My workload will be reduced to a realistic level.*

Taking Action

You Have Three Choices

Step 1. Identify cause of stress and check if there is a practical solution	→	Step 2. Change your thinking response	→	Step 3. Manage your stress responses in a more practical way

Step 1   First identify the cause of stress, then you can ask yourself: "Is there a practical solution? Can I remove the cause of stress or remove myself from it?" If not try ...

Step 2   Change your thinking response. You can examine the way you think about the problem and move from negative to positive thinking responses. But if you have become so entangled that you just can't change your negative thoughts then try to ...

Step 3   Manage your stress responses in a more positive way. You can now examine your stress responses and ensure that you are using more positive than negative coping responses.

Private Life

When you are confronted with any problem follow through this sequence to find a positive coping response if there is no practical solution.

Example

Identify cause of stress		*No time for myself. I'm always running around after other people.*
1	Is there a practical solution?	*Yes – I could work out a time-management plan and ensure I have a regular weekly slot to do what I want to do. I must make sure that I keep this time for myself.*
2	Can I change my thinking response?	
3	Can I manage my stress responses in a more positive way?	

Private Life

Example

Identify cause of stress

		My boyfriend is very domineering.
1	Is there a practical solution?	*No – I'm very in love with him and frightened of losing him.*
2	Can I change my thinking response?	*No – It's far too difficult for me to change quickly. I've always been dominated by people. I would need long term counselling to change my thinking.*
3	Can I change my stress response in a more positive way?	*Yes – My stress response to this situation is that I often can't sleep, I nag and I am frequently weepy... I could attend a course to develop my assertiveness skills. I could learn relaxation techniques to help me sleep and to control my weepiness.*

Private Life

Now identify two causes of stress in your private life and, following the format of the two previous examples, fill in the boxes.

Identify cause of stress

1   Is there a practical solution?

2   Can I change my thinking response?

3   How could I change my stress response?

Identify cause of stress

1   Is there a practical solution?

2   Can I change my thinking response?

3   How could I change my stress response?

Professional Life

Example

	Identify cause of stress	*'Back-biting' at work.*
1	Is there a practical solution?	*No – I don't want to leave, I enjoy my work.*
2	Can I change my thinking response?	*No – I'm too angry at the moment to change my thinking responses on my own.*
3	Can I change my stress response in a more positive way?	*Yes – My stress response at present is to get in a 'huff' and leave the room. The physical tension has affected my neck and given me headaches..... I could stay in the room and calmly tell the people concerned how I feel. I could join an aerobics class to release the physical tension.*

Professional Life

Example

	Identify cause of stress	*I get very nervous and tongue-tied when I have to speak to my boss.*
1	Is there a practical solution?	*No*
2	Can I change my thinking response?	*Yes – I must realise my boss isn't assessing me personally. He is only interested in exchanging information and ideas. I must realise that my fear is irrational and our meetings would be far more productive if I wasn't so self-concious.*
3	Can I change my stress response in a more positive way?	

Professional Life

Now identify two causes of stress at work and, following the format of the two previous examples, fill in the boxes.

Identify cause of stress

1   Is there a practical solution?

2   Can I change my thinking response?

3   How could I change my stress response?

Identify cause of stress

1   Is there a practical solution?

2   Can I change my thinking response?

3   How could I change my stress response?

Negative coping responses increase stress

Causes of Stress

↓

ill-health pain change travel	family pressures emotional pressures work pressures financial pressures	environmental pressures social pressures decision making phobias

↓

Stress can result in negative personal changes

↓ *for example*

Physical Changes	Thinking & Emotional Changes	Behavioural Changes
tension tiredness illness	poor concentration anxiety depression	irritability emotional outbursts poor eating habits drug & alcohol abuse

↓ *leads to*

ill-health psychosomatic illness	nervous breakdown insomnia	rushing from one thing to another becoming obsessional dependence on drugs and alcohol

↓ *which in turn leads to*

inability to cope with future pressures and stress
breakdown in relationships
feelings of physical disharmony
reduced productivity
prolonged mental illness
physical and emotional vulnerability
lack of fulfilment and loss of happiness

Positive coping responses reduce stress

Causes of Stress

↓

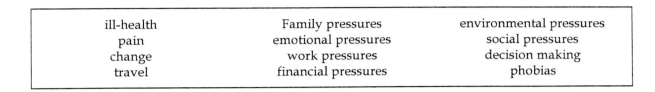

ill-health	Family pressures	environmental pressures
pain	emotional pressures	social pressures
change	work pressures	decision making
travel	financial pressures	phobias

↓

Making the following personal responses helps you to cope in a positive way

↓ _for example_

Physical Responses	Thinking & Emotional Respones	Behavioural Responses
healthy eating relaxation exercise	talking honestly to people learning to think positively	going to assertiveness course efficient use of time changing your circumstances

↓ _leads to_

better physical health	mental and emotional well-being	greater self confidence

↓ _which in turn leads to_

ability to cope with future pressures and stress healthier relationships feelings of physical well-being greater productivity increased happiness and fulfilment

Stress Proofing

Help your body cope with the effects of stress

The more healthy and physically fit you are, the better able your body will be to cope with the physical changes that occur during the stress response.

Exercise is also useful in helping discharge pent-up energy (often a residue of unrelieved stress) and frustration. In general, people who take regular exercise have more energy, feel better and are less susceptible to some of the stress-related illnesses.

The physical benefits of regular exercise are:

> it reduces blood pressure and blood sugar levels
> it improves the efficiency of the heart
> it releases muscle tension
> it helps keep joints flexible

Stress proof yourself through sport

There is a wide range of physical sports to choose from nowadays. Listed below are just some of the options available. Look through the list and choose a sport that you think you will enjoy. Persuade a friend to join with you, if you are shy of going alone, and determine to stick at it. It might be exhausting and difficult to start with, but don't give up. Think of the benefits and, in time, exercise will become a normal part of your life.

Tennis	Cycling
Badminton	Canoeing
Swimming	Sailing
Jogging	Bowling
Aerobics	Trampolining
Keep-Fit	Table Tennis
Horse riding	Netball
Squash	Basketball
Hockey	Skating
Gymnastics	Golf
Yoga	Karate

Stress proof yourself through your diet

An unhealthy diet can affect your body's ability to cope with stress and increase the chances of serious illness. It is important to ensure that your diet is well-balanced and includes sufficient quantities of all the main nutritional elements – i.e. protein, carbohydrates, fats, vitamins and minerals. Also, that the calorific value is correct for you and that you take in sufficient roughage to aid digestion – 18g of fibre is the recommended dietary intake per day.

Cut down on the intake of fat to maintain your blood cholesterol at a healthy level; one in four Britons runs an increased risk of heart disease because their blood cholesterol level is too high. It is, however, thought that polyunsaturates in spreading margarine are not so good for us after all and many nutrition experts now recommend the use of butter in moderation.

Avoid fried foods – grill them as a healthier alternative.

Eat plenty of fresh fruit and vegetables to provide the necessary vitamins and minerals. Steam or just lightly boil your vegetables.

Cut down on tea, coffee and cola which contain harmful chemicals and drink fresh fruit juices or water instead.

There are many types of grains, pulses (beans, lentils and peas) and vegetables available in shops now. Take time to investigate alternative food products and cooking methods to provide you with a healthy, balanced diet.

Stress proof yourself through sleep and relaxation

Lack of sleep increases the effects of stress because it undermines our ability to cope. If we are deprived of quality sleeping time we can become listless, depressed, irrational and over emotional. Although experts are still not certain of the function of sleep, they all agree that it is vital for a person's well-being.

Try to prepare yourself for sleep by observing the following rules:

1. Don't eat a meal prior to going to bed

2. Avoid stimulants like alcohol, coffee or cigarettes

3. Switch off mental activity at least half an hour before bedtime

4. Distract yourself from 'worries' with a book, television or relaxation techniques

5. Try to follow a regular sleeping pattern so that your body develops its own 'clock'

6. Avoid becoming dependent on sleeping tablets; if you have a problem sleeping, find the cause

Find a quiet time every day when you can relax for half an hour. Buy a magazine to read or treat yourself to a relaxing bath preparation and ensure that nobody disturbs you or encroaches on this time. If you find relaxation difficult enrol in a yoga class or buy a tape and learn relaxation techniques.

Relaxation Exercise

The following exercise is useful to refresh and relax you when you have a limited amount of time. Make sure that you will not be disturbed for ten minutes, take the phone off the hook, close the door and, if possible, dim the light. Settle yourself into a comfortable chair with armrests. Sit straight so that your thighs and back are fully supported.

Begin to breathe in and out slowly.

Sigh on the out-breaths and feel that you are releasing the tension from your body.

Do this several times then return to normal breathing.

Concentrate your attention onto your forehead, imagine it growing wider, feel your eyes sink deep into their sockets, let your cheeks soften and your jaw relax.

Imagine a smile on your face.

Now relax your shoulders, feel them drop.

Concentrate on your right arm and hand-feel the tension flow down your arm and out of your finger tips, allow them to relax and soften.

Repeat this for your left arm and hand.

Now become aware of your body, feel it growing softer and more relaxed.

Travel in your mind down your right leg to your right foot.

Feel the tension being released through your toes, feel your foot grow warm and heavy.

Repeat this for your left leg and foot.

Now that your body is relaxed concentrate on each breath and feel a sensation of peace flowing into you, feel yourself drifting in the gentle calmness surrounding you.

When you have enjoyed this sensation for several minutes you can gradually and gently bring your consciousness back to the present.

Open your eyes and stretch your whole body and then 'let go'. Repeat this a few times

Spiritual Well-being

The spiritual or inner self has been neglected in the western world in recent times, but eastern cultures still realise the value of developing this area.

Meditation, used frequently and regularly, is a very helpful aid in coping with stress as it provides the mental and physical resources we need. The aim of meditation is to increase 'awareness' and by focusing our attention on a single object or experience it helps us to:

1.   Increase our control over our thought processes

2.   Learn how to handle our emotions

3.   Train our attention

In time and with practice, meditation can become an invaluable means of dealing with the negative effects of stress on our minds and bodies.

Many people find that a strong spiritual belief provides them with inner resources and faith to cope with stressful situations. Furthermore they gain comfort and support from the people who share a similar belief. It can be a great source of hope and inspiration to know that an immortal and infallible god cares about you and can offer you help and understanding throughout the crises in your life.

Stress proof yourself with emergency coping strategies

At times of crises, for example when someone suddenly 'has a go' at you, you can learn to use an emergency coping strategy to prevent the stress response from being activated or to lessen its effect.

Don't panic – breathe deeply for a short time or count slowly to ten.

Tell yourself to keep calm.

Decide to deal with a problem later, once your emotions have calmed down.

Look for the funny side of a situation.

Set a time deadline when you will stop thinking about a problem.

Look for reasons behind other people's actions.

Take a check on your priorities.

Step outside the situation and take an objective look.

Ask the other person involved if you can both take time to reflect and resume discussion afterwards.

Don't get locked into a spiral of conflict, find a way of removing yourself.

Practise a ten minute relaxation technique.

Write down five rational and positive statements about a situation.

Private Life

Check list to help you cope with stress in your private life

Take care of your health	In future I am going to ...
Cut out or decrease smoking and drinking alcohol	
Take up a physical sport	
Ensure that your diet is healthy and well balanced	
Allow time every day for a period of relaxation	
Try and plan occasional weekend breaks or holidays to allow you to unwind	
Have a 'well woman' check-up with your G.P. to ensure that you have no medical problem	

Change your perspective	In future I will try to ...
Don't be pessimistic	
Focus on positive aspects to change a situation and don't allow negative thoughts to make you feel hopeless	
Change the way you view a problem and allow this change to influence your thinking	
Try to be more objective and look at a situation from 'outside'	
Write a list of positive statements and pin it up where you will see it	
Remember many problems only exist because we see them as such	

Private Life

Time management	In future I will ...
Learn how to say no to excessive demands on your time	
Concentrate on the important rather than the urgent	
Write out a weekly schedule that includes relaxation time and stick to it	
Learn how to make efficient use of your time	

Relationships	In future I am going to ...
Find out the root cause of any problems	
Ask advice from trusted friends or professionals	
Look for the good in other people	
Don't have too high expectations of other people, which they are unable to fulfil	
Ask yourself if you are contributing to the problem and change your behaviour accordingly	
Don't 'bottle up' negative feelings, discussion is the best way to solve relationship problems	

Private Life

Learn to cope with stress	In future I will ...
Learn to recognise the signs of stress in your body	
Practise emergency coping strategies	
Be determined to adopt positive ways of coping even if you have to join a self-help group or team or learn new behavioural skills e.g. assertiveness	
Determine that you will deal with destructive coping strategies e.g. alcohol, drug dependence	

Be prepared for change	In future I am going to ...
Have the courage to make fundamental changes in your life if your health and future happiness depend on these	
Plan a progressive schedule of 'small steps' if you can't face a 'massive leap'	
Be prepared and know how to deal with other people's negative reactions to your changes	
When the going gets tough, remind yourself of past unhappiness and focus on a better future	
Don't rush into easy solutions, make sure the changes you are initiating are really beneficial to you	

Private Life

Positive versus Negative	In future I will try to ...
Be optimistic – remember that problems can be solved Think positively, negative thoughts can only compound stress and make it worse Focus on yourself and your responses and behaviour - you can't change other people Don't adopt evasive coping strategies, e.g. pretending the problem doesn't exist, transposing feelings from the cause to some other object or person Ask yourself, "What is right for me, what makes me happy?" then aim for this goal	
Don't be side-tracked from your goal by outside pressures Don't give up if you encounter set-backs Learn how to cope with stress more effectively in the future Find out those personal character traits which tend to put you in stressful situations and learn how to change or moderate them	**In future I will not ...**

Professional Life

Check list to help you cope with stress in your professional life

Write down a positive statement in each box.

Assess your work	In future I need to ...
Recognise the symptoms of stress and what is causing them Assess the suitability of the work you are doing for your personal character traits, i.e. are you in the wrong job? Assess your personal attitude to your work, i.e. are you behaving in a manner that promotes stress? Ask yourself what you really want from work and see if your present employment fulfils these criteria	

Physical surroundings	I will try to effect the following changes ...
Do your physical surroundings provide a stress-free environment, e.g. are they too hot/cold, is there adequate ventilation? Are there factors in your environment which you find disturbing and stressful, e.g. lack of privacy, overcrowding, noise level? Do the facilities you have cause you, e.g. inadequate working materials, uncomfortable seating, badly designed working area, lack of resources? Find ways of making your physical environment more conducive to your work needs	

Professional Life

The role of management	In future I intend to ...
Develop relationships that are mutually respectful	
Ask for more information if stress is caused by insufficient knowledge	
Ask for positive feedback and progress reports to assess how you are doing and to experience success	
Keep in touch with management so that you know how they are thinking and what their expectations are	
Don't become trapped in a 'them' and 'us' situation	
Ensure that you have the support of management in what you are doing	

Work ethos	In future I will ...
Be clear about the boundaries of your responsibility	
Don't harbour negative thoughts about issues or policies which are contrary to your moral standards - find ways to discuss them and find agreeable solutions	
Make sure that you are happy about accepting any changes that are initiated	
Concentrate on promoting positive ideas of behaviour and standards	

Professional Life

Positive versus Negative	In future I will ...
Don't allow stressful situations to build up, deal with them promptly	
Avoid areas which you know will cause stress – discuss these with your boss if necessary	
Concentrate on areas that you enjoy and try and develop these	
Don't run away from stressful situations by absenteeism	
Assess your progress regularly to make sure that you still have your priorities right	**In future I will no longer ...**
If you no longer enjoy work find out why and take action	
Be positive and have clear aims and goals – know where you are going and be in control of your life	
Never feel that you are 'stuck' in a stressful situation – there is always a solution to every problem	

3

Developing Assertiveness in your Private and Professional Life

Developing Assertiveness

Introduction

Considerable research evidence, plus our own experience in helping women on assertiveness courses, suggests that much non-assertive behaviour has its source in low self-esteem. We have seen in previous chapters how low self-esteem can lead to stress and anxiety in many situations. When you start to feel worried and on edge about certain events, then the people involved in those events may become threatening too. We could think of this downward spiral in the following sequence.

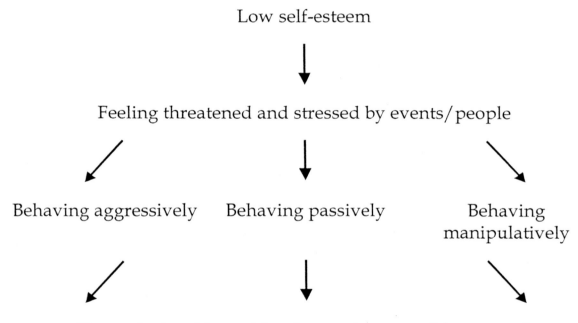

Low self-esteem

↓

Feeling threatened and stressed by events/people

Behaving aggressively   Behaving passively   Behaving manipulatively

Poor relationships with others at home and/or at work

The first two sections looked at how you can build self-esteem and cope well with stress. We will now consider some important practical steps using assertive skills which you can take to improve the quality of your private and professional relationships and thus further develop your personal power.

Research has shown us that if we have satisfactory and secure relationships at home and at work, it is likely that we will be:

★ happier
★ fitter
★ less stressed
★ more confident and outgoing
★ less depressed
★ able to take risks

Even though satisfying relationships are vital to our well-being, we seldom take positive steps to maintain or improve them. Most of us take our relationships for granted, allowing things to drift along, becoming fatalistic about situations which upset us and feeling powerless to make changes.

Have you got the kind of relationships you want and deserve?

Do you sometimes wish for a more fulfilling relationship with your partner?

Do you want to put a long-standing friendship on a different footing?

Do you want to change the way you relate to your family?

Would you like to develop better working relationships?

One of the most positive and constructive ways to enjoy more satisfying relationships is by developing assertive skills.

What is Assertiveness?

Assertiveness is about developing relationships based on honesty and openness. It is a way of behaving which helps us to express our thoughts, feelings and beliefs in direct, honest and helpful ways. It also means that we allow others to express their views and feelings in turn to us, and show respect for their point of view.

Assertive behaviour is behaviour which relies on

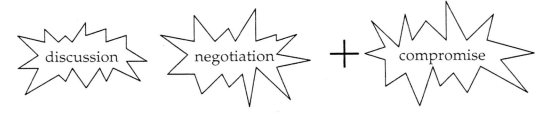

It is an alternative to *passive, manipulative* or *aggressive* behaviour.

Each of us is passive, manipulative, aggressive or assertive in different situations. The first step in developing assertive skills is learning to distinguish between these different ways of behaving. Read though the descriptions below to see if you can recognise any of these behaviours in yourself or others.

Aggressive Behaviour

Is loud. Is forceful. Sets out to 'win'. 'Proves' superiority by putting others down. Attacks when threatened. Uses verbal, sometimes physical, violence and abuse. 'Makes' others defensive, aggressive, hurt, humiliated, resentful, afraid.

Passive Behaviour

Opts out and avoids confrontation. Has difficulty in making decisions and taking responsibility for choices. Feels a victim of unfairness. Blames others for things that happen. Envies others their abilities, assets and luck. Lacks willpower. Is apologetic. Puts self down and refuses compliments. 'Makes' others frustrated, resentful, exasperated, guilty.

Manipulative Behaviour

Is indirectly aggressive and hurtful. Needs to be in control. Does not trust self or others. Is skilled in deception. Avoids confrontation with risk of rejection and hurt. 'Makes' others confused, frustrated, guilty.

Assertive Behaviour

Is able to accept positive and negative qualities in self and others. Accepts responsibility for own action, decisions and choices. Can ask directly for own needs to be met, accepting risk of rejection. Is sensitive to others' needs. Is not overwhelmed by rejection. Is not dependent on others' approval. Responds sincerely to others. Accepts that he/she has rights. Accepts that others have rights. Is self-confident. 'Makes' others trust, respect, feel comfortable.

Think how you might react in the following situation

You have been asked to work late by your boss who can be very difficult to work with. You have arranged to meet a friend from work that evening, and although it would be possible to change the arrangement you don't want to. How would you react?

Put a tick in the box that best describes your likely action, thoughts and feelings.

	Passive	Aggressive	Manipulative	Assertive
Action	I say 'yes' – I can't say 'no' because he might fly into a temper/see me as uncooperative/fail to promote me.	Tell him to find someone else – how can he be so inconsiderate!	Tell him I've got a dreadful headache and I must get back home as soon as possible.	Tell him I can't work late as I have arranged to meet a friend – I will willingly get in early tomorrow to help.
✔				
Thoughts & Feelings	I'm such a wimp! I wish I could stand up for myself but I want him to think well of me. I feel used and manipulated by him and disappointed with myself.	How dare he say that to me! Who does he think he is! I feel angry and resentful.	I wish I didn't have to lie my way out of situations. He probably doesn't believe me anyway. I feel uncomfortable and dissatisfied with myself.	I feel satisfied that I was honest and direct and offered him a compromise. I feel relaxed and pleased with how I acted.
✔				

Private Life

How assertive are you in your relationship with your partner?

Decide how you would react in the following situations.

Put a tick in the appropriate box. When completed find out your results on page 118

A. Your partner is always late when meeting you in town. He always apologises but it happens every time.

Do you say

1	2	3	4
It's OK – I don't mind waiting – don't worry about it.	Why on earth can't you be on time! I sometimes think you're late on purpose.	I feel angry when you keep me waiting every time we arrange to meet. I'd appreciate it if you'd be on time in future.	I was worried something had happened to you.

B. You have bought a new dress for a special occasion – one which you are really pleased with. Your partner says it doesn't suit you at all.

Do you

1	2	3	4
Ask him exactly why it doesn't suit you. Get other people's opinions too.	Feel upset and take it back to the shop.	Wait till he's going out somewhere and tell him he looks a mess.	Tell him you couldn't care less what he thinks since he's clueless about fashion.

C. You feel very annoyed with your partner because he put you down in front of work colleagues earlier in the day.

Do you

1	2	3	4
Give him a mouthful about his ignorance.	Don't speak about it at all but behave in a very offhand way e.g. sulking, not speaking, cold shoulder.	Explain to him exactly how you are feeling and why.	Go and talk to your best friend/mother /sister about it and get if off your chest.

D. You have arranged to meet a friend for lunch in town and you are looking forward to having a good heart to heart on your own. Your partner suddenly suggests he'd like to join you as he's free over lunch.

Do you

1	2	3	4
Agree that it would be fine for him to join you but feel disappointed.	Tell him 'no' and explain that you are looking forward to seeing your friend alone on this occasion.	Tell him you'd like him to develop his own friendships and stop following you around.	Say that your friend has something private to disclose and might feel let down if anyone else was there.

E. You are not in the mood for sex and your partner starts to make love to you.

Do you

1	2	3	4
Say you're sorry but you've got a 'head-ache' or 'cystitis'.	Join in for the sake of peace and quiet.	Tell him you are not feeling like sex tonight.	Start a row about inconsiderate behaviour.

F.   You start to talk about your day at work. Your partner carries on reading the paper apparently taking no notice.

Do you

1	2	3	4
Tell him that you feel hurt when he doesn't listen to how your day's been and you would like him to put the paper down to talk to you.	Leave the room to go and have a silent fume.	Have a rant that he never listens to how your day has been, but you spend hours listening to him.	Change the topic of conversation to something else.

Private Life

How assertive are you with family and friends?

Put a tick in the appropriate box. When completed find out your results on page 118

A.   You have lent one of your friends money a month ago and s/he hasn't mentioned it. You would like it repaid.

Do you

1	2	3	4
Say nothing to him/her but refuse any invitations to go anywhere until you are paid back.	Drop hints about being hard up.	Say that you lent him/her money a month ago and you would like it repaid as soon as possible.	Apologise about having to ask. Say you are sure it's not been forgotten, that you are not really in a hurry for it – but if s/he could remember sometime you'd be grateful.

B.   Your mother invites you for a 'family' occasion but you want to refuse as she's also invited your aunt with whom you've had a major disagreement.

Do you

1	2	3	4
Agree to go as it's what is expected of you.	Say you know they'll understand but your work is piling up and you really can't spare the time without risking your job/health sanity.	Flatly refuse the invitation.	Say although you want to see them you won't be coming as you don't want to meet your aunt just now. Could you come on another occasion?

114

C.   A friend asks to borrow your evening dress for a special occasion. You do not like the idea of lending it because several people you know well will be going too, and you have only worn it once yourself. You want to refuse.

Do you

1	2	3	4
Say I feel mean saying this but I'd rather not lend it out until I've worn it more myself.	Let her borrow it but feel really resentful that she's asked.	Tell her your sister's borrowed it and you haven't a clue when you'll get it back.	Tell her she's got cheek to ask as you've only worn it once yourself.

D.   Your friend invites you to go for supper as you've said you are not going out. However you have planned your evening and you want to spend it alone.

Do you

1	2	3	4
Say you can't come because you are expecting an important phone call/feeling too shattered (or any other appropriate excuse)	Say you can't be bothered to make the necessary arrangements at such short notice.	Go anyway because you'd feel mean to refuse without a 'real' excuse.	Say thank you for asking, however you've planned for ages to have an evening on your own tonight.

E. A friend travels with you to work in your car twice a week and you want to ask for a contribution to the petrol.

Do you

1	2	3	4
Say nothing and wonder if you are being mean for asking because you aren't going out of your way to give the lift.	Begin to be less reliable about being on time so you can start an argument about the arrangements to raise the issue of the petrol costs.	Say you've been meaning to ask for a while now if they would pay something towards the petrol costs.	Make hints about the cost of petrol and hope it will sink in.

F. A member of your family criticises your appearance and tells you that you are putting on too much weight. Their shape leaves a lot to be desired!

Do you

1	2	4	3
Tell them to mind their own business.	Feel upset and worry how you might look to other people.	Ignore the comments and find opportunities to make snide remarks later.	Tell them you are happy with your shape and how you look. Ask them where they think you should start first!

Professional Life

How assertive are you with work colleagues?

Put a ✔ in the appropriate box   *When completed check your score on page 121*

		Never	Rarely	Sometimes	Always
1	If I am unsure of what should be done with work I have been given, I can ask for assistance from others.				
2	When there is an opportunity for promotion I can put myself forward.				
3	If someone criticises me unfairly or puts me down in front of colleagues, I can raise the topic for discussion with him/her.				
4	I take well criticism which is deserved eg. lateness, forgetting deadlines etc.				
5	I can ask for salary increases when I think I deserve it.				
6	If I am asked to do something at work which I feel is unfair, too difficult, outside the terms of the contract, I can say 'no' politely with excuses.				
7	I can praise people for work well done without feeling embarrassed.				
8	I can give criticism when it is deserved without aggression or apology.				
9	If a work colleague is bossy or domineering I make sure I don't ignore it but deal with the situation.				
10	I am able to make a point in a meeting in front of several work colleagues.				
11	If someone asks me my opinion I am happy to tell them even though its against what most people think.				
12	If I experience sexual harassment I can tell the person calmly that I find the behaviour offensive.				
13	I can deal easily and effectively with people in authority at work.				

Scores for Questionnaires

Relationships with Partner

A

1	2	3	4
P	Agg	Ass	M

Your Result (P, Agg, Ass, M)

....

B

1	2	3	4
Ass	P	M	Agg

....

C

1	2	3	4
Agg	M	Ass	P

....

D

1	2	3	4
P	Ass	Agg	M

....

E

1	2	3	4
M	P	Ass	Agg

....

F

1	2	3	4
Ass	M	Agg	P

....

Relationships with Family/Friends

A

1	2	3	4
Agg	M	Ass	P

Your Result (P, Agg, Ass, M)

....

B

1	2	3	4
P	M	Agg	Ass

....

C

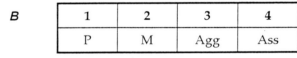

1	2	3	4
Ass	P	M	Agg

....

D

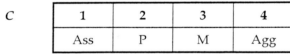

1	2	3	4
M	Agg	P	Ass

....

E

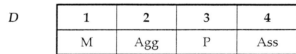

1	2	3	4
P	Agg	Ass	M

....

F

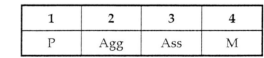

1	2	3	4
Agg	P	M	Ass

....

Mostly "Agg's"

You may be seen as loud and forceful, as someone who stands up for herself. Often you **do** get your way because people are frightened of challenging you. You tend to be very competitive and so keen to score that you forget to consider the other person's point of view or acknowledge their feelings. They may feel angry, hurt or humiliated by you but you may never know this as they learn to hide their feelings from you. Sometimes you may provoke an aggressive response but you usually find one to top it! Because you like to win at everything and want to be seen as tough at all costs, you may feel the need to be constantly watchful. You may regularly feel angry, irritated, hot and bothered and unappreciated. You are losing a lot of energy in your determination to win and putting all your relationships at risk. You have learned to cope with other people by being aggressive but you can decide to change the way you react. Recognise that there is an assertive option and that these skills can be learned.

Mostly "M's"

You are skilled at getting your own way with others and wriggling out of difficult situations but you are not direct in your approach because you are frightened of confrontation. Although you tell yourself you are protecting others it is usually a way of protecting yourself. You need to be in control and often confuse and frustrate people because they are unsure of your real feelings and intentions. Maybe you have learned to use subtle devices to get your own way and these usually work for you, but others may end up feeling used or compromised. You can also make other people feel guilty and uncomfortable if they have displeased you. Your relationships may suffer because people are never sure of the real you and don't trust you with their real concerns. Superficially you may **seem** to approve of them, but they may detect an undercurrent of disapproval. You don't really develop the kind of close relationships you would like. You regularly feel unhappy with yourself, misunderstood, guilty and ashamed. You need to learn to be more direct and open in your relationships and let others get to know the real you!

Mostly "P's"

You spend much of your time going along with what others want and what others **tell** you you want, for the sake of peace and quiet. Gradually you may opt out of making decisions and taking responsibility for choices in your life completely. Because other people feel forced into making decisions for you, they may feel frustrated and resentful. You hate confrontations and avoid them at all costs even if it means causing real upset to yourself. Giving in all the time may backfire on you because your 'never mind me' nature is often unappreciated and people may begin to treat you like a doormat.

You may feel hard done by and that good things happen to everyone but you. People help you up to a point but may get fed up with your negative outlook. You often put yourself down and find it difficult to acknowledge the nice things people do say about you.

You may regularly feel shy, stressed, inadequate, unhappy and guilty. You may find yourself being put last by others because you constantly put yourself last. You have learned to cope with life the best way you feel able but you need to start giving yourself more consideration, learn to know what you want and practise being more assertive.

Mostly "Ass's"

You are confident in yourself and regularly demonstrate that you can balance your own and others' needs. You respect other people and accept your own positive and negative qualities so that you don't need to put other people down to feel comfortable with yourself. You feel in charge of yourself - your actions and your choices. If you want something from other people you don't become aggressive, demanding or whining in your request; you can ask directly for what you need. You recognise your right to be listened to, consulted and involved in decision making. If people do treat you badly or refuse your request, you don't feel let down, bitter or rejected. Your self-esteem is high and you deal with their unreasonable behaviour in an honest and direct way.

You regularly feel assured, confident and happy; well able to deal effectively with your relationships. You are likely to build up strong, close friendships because people trust you and respect your integrity. Your friends are likely to treat you in a similarly assertive way.

Some women will identify with one description, others with two and many with all four at different times! It is interesting to see if you can identify a pattern in the way you relate to others. Are you, for example, an aggressive partner and a passive daughter? Once you can recognise how you are relating then you can start to make choices and changes.

How assertive are you with work colleagues?

How to score   Give yourself: 5 points for always

2 points for sometimes

1 point for rarely

0 points for never

Score 50 – 65

You are confident and assertive in your approach to situations at work, and well able to accept positive and negative qualities in self and others. You can ask for what you want from others without worrying what they might say in reply. You can stand up for yourself and your opinions, express your feelings openly and honestly without being aggressive. You are prepared to accept responsibility for your own action, decisions and choices. Keep working on assertiveness and learning more about the skills to retain this high quality of interaction with others.

Score 35 – 49

Although you can be assertive in many situations you tend to have 'problem' areas. It may be, for example, that you find difficulty in asserting yourself in groups or with people in authority. Try to identify those situations with which you have difficulty, and using the ideas which follow, identify the assertive skills which you need to practise to improve the way you deal with work colleagues in these situations.

Score 16 – 34

You are unable to be consistent in your assertive behaviour. Some days you are confident about your work, making decisions, stating your views, but the next day something goes wrong and you behave unassertively. You then worry about what other people may think, become unsure of your work and feel vulnerable to the slightest criticism. It is important that you learn to be consistent in your relationships at work, so that people know where they are with you. Choose one area to work on initially which is relatively easy to tackle and, using ideas in this chapter, practise using assertive skills to effect changes in the way you relate.

Score 0 – 15

You find it difficult to assert yourself at work, often feel unable to do or say what you really want. You may be afraid to assert your rights as you worry that people may see you as awkward. You worry too, that if you tried to make a stand about things which concern you, you may become emotional or angry. It is important that you start to communicate more effectively. Using the information in this chapter discuss with a friend how you might start to use assertive skills to develop more fulfilling relationships at work. Practise by using role play initially and start with a relatively easy situation.

Possible Areas of Difficulty in Developing Assertiveness

Looking at your scores and the answers to previous questionnaires, try to identify possible areas of difficulty which you may experience in your private and/or professional relationships.

Am I able to say 'No'?		Examples
	at work	No, I cannot work late tonight
		No I cannot give you a lift
		No I cannot help with the Christmas Party
	at home	No I cannot see you at the weekend
		No I don't want to go to bed
Am I able to express my anger?		
	at work	I get angry when you don't give me enough information to work with
		I feel really annoyed when you don't listen to me
		I get really irritated when you turn up late
	at home	I feel furious when you drive so fast
		I get cross inside when you're always complaining about things
Am I able to express my positive thoughts and feelings?		
	at work	I think you made a really good presentation today
		I like the way you use everyone's name
		I appreciate your cheerfulness
	at home	I do appreciate your letters to me
		I do like your hair

Am I able to express my negative feelings?

	at work	*I feel really upset about my interview* *I feel very uncomfortable when you make comments like that*
	at home	*I feel bitter about your mother's interference* *I feel scared when you get angry* *I resent all this time spent watching television*

Am I able to state what I believe?

	at work	*I think it would be better of we changed the meetings from Thursdays in future* *I disagree with Mr Holt about the plans for next week*
	at home	*I don't agree that we are getting on fine* *I think the discussion about our finances has gone on long enough*

Am I able to ask for what I want?

	at work	*I would like you to give me some feedback on my work this year* *I would like you to ask me well ahead if you need me at the weekend*
	at home	*I would like you to visit us during the week rather than the weekend* *I would like some more information about the treatment I'm receiving for my illness*

Many women find that they are able to behave assertively with their work colleagues but find it difficult to say what they want to with their partner and/or friends. Others find the opposite; they are confident and assertive with their close friends and become tongue-tied when dealing with people at work.

Your Rights

Before you start on the practical exercises which follow, it is important to consider your basic human rights. In our relationships these may be thought of as ways in which we might reasonably expect to treat and be treated by each other.

★ ## I have the right to be myself

Sometimes you may feel swamped by all your responsibilities but it is important to remember to make time for your own personal wants and needs.

★ ## I have the right to be treated as an equal

On occasions where we feel less sure of ourselves we may allow ourselves to be treated as less capable or less intelligent than we are.

★ ## I have the right to an opinion

It may be difficult to voice an opinion which is contradictory to the rest of the family/friends/work colleagues views, but we have the right to express it.

★ ## I have the right to express my feelings

It is very important to be able to identify how we feel at the time of the event and let others know how it is affecting us.

★ ## I have the right to make a choice

It is important to feel free to make choices because we want to do or not to do something without having to justify our choice on other grounds.

★ ## I have the right to be wrong

Many of us feel overwhelmed with anxiety when we make mistakes but it is important to recognise that we are not infallible, and that to make errors is human and natural. It may be unfortunate but it need not throw us into a turmoil of self-deceit.

★ ## I have the right to say 'I don't understand'

Asking for an explanation when you are confused can be difficult (especially when everyone else seems to be taking things in) but you cannot know and understand everything. You are perfectly entitled to ask for clarification without feeling stupid.

★ ## I have the right to ask for what I want

Many of us do not ask for things in a straightforward manner. We drop hints, make suggestions, hedge round the subject, hoping that someone will get the message. We feel that the request will be rejected. We worry about causing inconvenience to others or being seen as a nuisance. We must remember that we have the right to make requests of other people.

Being clear about and accepting your rights and other people's rights provides you with a good basis for assertive behaviour.

Continually consult these basic rights in your quest for more assertive relationships.

Situations in my Private Life when I would like to be more Assertive

Keeping your rights in mind consider eight situations in your private life where you would like to behave more assertively. This might be with a partner, family, friends, acquaintances. Give each situation a score on the scale 0 – 10; 10 denoting situations which you would find most difficulty with, 1–2 indicating situations which are less difficult for you to tackle.

		Score 0 – 10
Examples:	Saying 'No' to my mother	8
	Asking for my money back for family goods	4
	Complaining about the loud music from my neighbours	3
	Asking my partner to be more demonstrative to me	9
Situation 1		
Situation 2		
Situation 3		
Situation 4		
Situation 5		
Situation 6		
Situation 7		
Situation 8		

Situations in my Professional Life when I would like to be more Assertive

List eight situations in your professional life where you would like to behave more assertively. This might be with senior colleagues, junior colleagues, ancillary staff, clients, in small groups, in large groups.

		Score 0 – 10
Examples:	Asking my boss for a salary review Being firm with customers Asking people not to smoke Speaking up at meetings	8 4 3 9
Situation 1		
Situation 2		
Situation 3		
Situation 4		
Situation 5		
Situation 6		
Situation 7		
Situation 8		

How to Improve Your Assertive Skills in your Private and Professional Relationships

There are Six Steps to Basic Assertiveness

STEP 1	IDENTIFY	WHAT THE PROBLEM IS – BE SPECIFIC
STEP 2	SAY	WHAT YOU FEEL CLEARLY, DIRECTLY AND WITH CONVICTION. NAME THE PERSON
STEP 3	SAY	WHAT YOU WANT TO HAPPEN AND ASK HOW THEY FEEL ABOUT IT
STEP 4	LISTEN	TO THE RESPONSE
STEP 5	RESTATE	YOUR POSITION GIVING CONSIDERATION TO THEIR RESPONSE
STEP 6	TRY TO REACH AN AGREEMENT	

Being assertive does not always come easily or naturally to us. Start by tackling less difficult and less sensitive situations first and **practise** being assertive on your own, or with a friend. (Role playing offers the most effective way of helping you to develop the technique). You will soon feel more competent and comfortable with this new way of communicating.

Situation in my Private Life where I would like to behave more Assertively

Choose one situation from your private life where you would like to be more assertive. Using the example below as a guide, fill in the questionnaire on the next page.

Example

Step 1 – Identify the problem. Be specific. Name the person

> *Chris, I spend half of every Saturday cleaning the flat.*

Step 2 – Say what you feel clearly, directly and with conviction

> *I feel irritated that most of the cleaning is left to me.*

Step 3 – Say what you want to happen and ask how they feel

> *I would like us to share the cleaning and I suggest that we draw up a rota or find some other way to share the work out more fairly. How do you feel about this?*

Step 4 – Listen to the response

> *I think you spend far too much time cleaning! It doesn't take half a day to clean this place.*

Step 5 – Restate your case giving consideration to their response

> *I understand that you don't think it's necessary to spend so much time cleaning. However, I feel resentful that it's mostly left to me and in future I suggest we draw up a list of jobs which need doing and share them out equally.*

Step 6 – Try to reach an agreement

Situation in my Private Life where I would like to be more Assertive

Step 1 – Identify the problem. Be specific. Name the person

```



```

Step 2 – Say what you feel clearly, directly and with conviction

```



```

Step 3 – Say what you want to happen and ask how they feel

```



```

Step 4 – Listen to the response
(Try to anticipate this so you can practise your restatement)

```



```

Step 5 – Restate your case giving consideration to their response

```



```

Step 6 – Try to reach an agreement
(Try to think about the compromise you would be prepared to accept and write this in the box)

```



```

Situation in my Professional Life where I would like to be more Assertive

Example

Step 1 – Identify the problem. Be specific. Name the person

> *Joan, you smoke in my room at lunchtime at least once a week.*

Step 2 – Say what you feel clearly, directly and with conviction

> *I feel very uncomfortable with cigarette smoke.*

Step 3 – Say what you want to happen and ask how they feel

> *I would prefer it if you didn't have a cigarette in my room. I do hope you understand how I feel.*

Step 4 – Listen to the response

> *Why on earth have you never said anything before. You should have said something. I thought you didn't mind.*

Step 5 – Restate your case giving consideration to their response

> *You are right, I should have mentioned it before but I felt awkward saying it because I know how you enjoy a smoke.*

Step 6 – Try to reach an agreement

> *Agreed that cigarettes wouldn't be smoked in my room.*

Situation in my Professional Life where I would like to be more Assertive

Step 1 – Identify the problem. Be specific. Name the person

Step 2 – Say what you feel clearly, directly and with conviction

---

Step 3 – Say what you want to happen and ask how they feel

Step 4 – Listen to the response
(Try to anticipate this so you can practise your restatement)

Step 5 – Restate your case giving consideration to their response

---

Step 6 – Try to reach an agreement
(Try to think about the compromise you would be prepared to accept and write this in the box)

Becoming relaxed and confident in using assertive techniques takes time and effort. Every time you are reticent and laid back or lose your temper and become angry, it would have been possible to behave **assertively** instead. Remind yourself by reading the list below about the advantages of behaving assertively.

- ★ *You will feel good about yourself and your behaviour*

- ★ *You will be able to accept praise and handle criticism*

- ★ *You will be able to communicate your needs more openly and honestly*

- ★ *You will be able to view mistakes in a positive light and learn from them*

- ★ *You will be able to take risks*

- ★ *You will be able to deal with problems more easily*

- ★ *You will feel more comfortable and in charge of your life*

In the exercises you have done so far you were practising assertive skills in situations where **you** initiated the action. On many occasions you are required to **respond** to the action of other people, e.g. when they request something of you, when they praise, criticise or confront you, when you are asked your opinion. Often these situations pose more problems for us because we are put on the spot and forced to reply without having had time to prepare ourselves.

To help you to practise using assertive skills we have chosen a number of situations which arise fairly often. Because most of us meet at least one of the situations described every day there will be plenty of opportunity for you to practise them. With each situation we give a number of guidelines for behaving assertively in them. The situations we will deal with are:

SAYING NO in our private and professional relationships

GIVING AND RECEIVING PRAISE AND COMPLIMENTS in our private and professional relationships

HANDLING CRITICISM in our private and professional relationships

HANDLING AGGRESSION in our private and professional relationships

In all these situations we will be emphasising the importance of your *ACTIVE LISTENING* at the beginning of the interaction.

Saying 'No' in your Private and Professional Life

Think back to a situation with your partner, family, friends or work colleagues when you found yourself doing something which you didn't want to do. Does this occur often?

Tick the boxes that apply to you.

What type of request do you find difficult to refuse?

Lending something? ☐

Invitations you want to refuse? ☐

Opinions you don't wish to share? ☐

Information you don't want to give? ☐

Whom do you find it difficult to refuse?

Older people? ☐

Family? ☐

Partner? ☐

Work colleagues? ☐

Authority Figures? ☐

Children? ☐

When do you find it difficult to refuse a request?

In a group? ☐

On the phone? ☐

In a meeting? ☐

When you are relaxed? ☐

In someone else's house? ☐

Private Life

Chose a situation in your private life when you said 'yes' when you would have preferred to say 'no'

Describe the situation

Example	Your situation and the request
A friend was booking her holiday and asked me to go with her.	

How I feel about the situation

Example	Your situation and the request
I didn't want to go because I prefer to go with a group and although I enjoy her company, to be alone with her for two weeks would be rather boring.	

Why I said Yes

Example	Your situation and the request
I hadn't arranged anything. I felt mean saying 'no' as her partner has just left her.	

What I would have liked to do and say

Example	Your situation and the request
I would have liked to refuse and say "No – although I haven't made plans for the summer and I do enjoy your company, I would prefer to go away with a group!"	

Professional Life

Chose a situation in your professional life when you said 'yes' when you would have preferred to say 'no'

Describe the situation

Example	Your situation and the request
I was asked to write the minutes for a meeting. I was one of a minority of women – I am always asked to do so.	

How I feel about the situation

Example	Your situation and the request
I felt angry that I was asked because I am a woman. I feel I cannot contribute to the meeting as effectively if I have to write the minutes.	

Why I said Yes

Example	Your situation and the request
I was worried that they would think I was being awkward if I refused. I thought I might sound pathetic or 'feminist'.	

What I would have liked to do and say

Example	Your situation and the request
"No - I always write the minutes which makes it difficult to take part in the meeting. I would appreciate someone else taking a turn."	

Saying 'No' in your Private and Professional Life

Saying 'no' clearly and definitely can be difficult for many of us. We worry that we may appear insensitive, rude, selfish or pig-headed. We may be concerned that the other person will think badly of us or become aggressive.

Remember, other people have the right to ask but we have the right to say 'no'.

What might happen if we say 'yes' when we mean 'no':

★ *You may take on too much and find life and work too stressful*

★ *You may find yourself spending hours extricating yourself from unwanted commitments*

★ *You may feel resentful about becoming involved with something which you wanted to refuse*

★ *You may have negative feelings about yourself for not being able to refuse the request*

Guidelines for saying 'No' when you want to refuse a request

★   *Notice your reaction and trust it*

Your body will let you know whether you feel like agreeing or refusing (a certain sinking feeling in the stomach will be evident).

★   *Give yourself time*

If you start to hesitate say ...   "could you give me some time to think about it"
                                          or
                                        "could you tell me something more about it"

★   *Keep the reply short (but not abrupt)*

Don't use long-winded sentences filled with excuses and apologies, e.g. "Well I'm not really sure, I can't really find anyone to look after the cat and I'm not sure if I'm going to the dentist **this** Thursday or next and anyway I'm not a good person to ask".

★   *Give the real reason for refusing*

Don't invent an excuse – it makes you feel guilty and is often recognised as such by the other person.

★   *Practise saying 'no' at the beginning of the statement*

          No, I cannot look after the hamster
          No, I prefer not to look after the hamster
          No, I'm not happy to look after the hamster

This is far preferable to "I'm not very good with hamsters". People like to know where they stand and a clear 'no' makes everyone's life easier.

How do you feel when someone doesn't turn up who said 'yes' initially or lets you down at the last minute with a 'headache'?

★   *Do not hover around after you've said 'no'*

This only encourages the other person to try to change your mind.

★   *Do acknowledge your feelings*

e.g.   I find it difficult to have to say 'no'
                I feel guilty for not offering to help
                I feel ungrateful to have to refuse

★   *Ask how they feel and if possible offer an alternative*

Sometimes people may be hurt, feel rejected or annoyed by your refusal but remember that **you are refusing the request, not rejecting the person**

You may feel guilty for refusing requests assertively at first but it will get easier with practice. The benefits from being able to say 'no' clearly, directly and honestly will be well worth it.

Look again at your completed exercise on page 134 and check that your reply follows these guidelines.

Giving and Receiving Praise and Compliments

Many people find it difficult to make positive and appreciative comments. They worry that their compliment will be taken the wrong way making others feel embarrassed or awkward. At work people become concerned that they may be seen as 'soft' or a 'pushover' and mistakenly believe that praising people will curtail effort. In personal relationships people frequently worry that others will suspect their motives if they show their appreciation in a positive way. Yet the opposite is true. People enjoy and benefit from receiving praise and compliments. They learn from the feedback given. They are far more likely to feel positive about themselves, to be cooperative, to feel appreciated and consequently put far more effort into their work and relationships.

Sadly all too often we forget to tell people how we feel, thank them for things they have done, and show our appreciation for their concern and loyalty.

How to Give Praise and Compliments Assertively

★   *Look directly at the other person in a relaxed way*

★   *Lowering your eyes indicates that you are embarrassed but too staring eye contact may make them feel uncomfortable*

★   *Keep your message clear and brief, don't be too flowery and don't apologise e.g. I hope you don't mind my saying but ...*

★   *Use 'I' statements –*   *I like the way you ...*

                               I enjoyed reading your account of ...

                               I'm pleased with ...

★   *Make it specific –*   *Say 'I liked the way you organised the meeting and allowed everyone a say'*

               rather than –   *'you did well this afternoon'*

This type of feedback is more likely to encourage the other person to know exactly what it was they did well and therefore be more able to repeat the performance

Receiving Praise and Compliments

People frequently behave defensively when they receive praise. They may dismiss the other person's compliment in a passive or flippant manner – Oh it wasn't **that** good, or I don't really rate it myself – it didn't take me a minute. Oh this dress – I've had it ages! This type of response has the effect of putting the other person down and certainly reduces the chance that they will give compliments next time.

How to Receive Praise Assertively

★   *Thank the giver*   –   *Thank you Jane*

★   *Keep the response short*   –   *I'm glad you like it*
                                        I'm glad you thought it went well

★   *Accept the praise*   –   *I've liked it for ages but couldn't afford it till now*
                                        I was pleased with the reception too

Private Life

Think of a situation in your private life where you wish you had given a compliment or said something appreciative to someone, but didn't.

Situation

Example	Your situation
My partner always makes a special meal on Fridays for us and I don't make much comment.	

What I would like to have said

Example	Your situation
I really appreciate the trouble you go to to cook something different each week.	

Why I didn't say it

Example	Your situation
He never compliments me on preparing our meals and I suppose I feel he should make this effort as I usually cook the rest of the time.	

Consequence

Example	Your situation
He doesn't feel appreciated. I feel mean for not saying anything. It doesn't help him to praise me.	

Professional Life

Think of a situation in your professional life where you wish you had given a compliment or said something appreciative to someone, but didn't.

Situation

Example	Your situation
My boss was very appreciative of extra time I had put in for her one weekend and sent me a thank-you letter and flowers. I just said a short 'thanks'.	

What I would like to have said

Example	Your situation
Thank you very much for your letter and gift. It makes me feel that extra effort is really appreciated here.	

Why I didn't say it

Example	Your situation
I thought she might think I was 'going over the top'.	

Consequence

Example	Your situation
I felt I never really let her know what I thought and worried that she thinks I took the gift for granted as my 'right'.	

Handling Criticism in your Private and Professional Relationships

In our close relationships and in our interaction with work colleagues, most of us will have received and given criticism. Nevertheless, most of us remain extremely vulnerable to any form of criticism directed towards us. We store up detailed memories of critical comments from childhood experiences and past relationships which can still have a powerful effect on us today. We label people who criticise us as unfair, overpowering or untrustworthy. When we are criticised we invariably end up feeling attacked, hurt, angry or neglected. We seldom use the criticism constructively or benefit in anyway from the experience.

Learning to deal with criticism assertively is important. We must try to recognise that criticism well received can be useful and constructive and need not be experienced as rejection or an attack.

Usually an aspect of our behaviour is being criticised and not our total personality.

Receiving Criticism in my Personal Relationships

Think of a recent experience in your personal relationships (with a partner, friend or family member) when you received criticism and dealt with it in an unsatisfactory way.

Describe the situation

Example	*Your situation*
I was late meeting my partner in town.	

What was said to you?

Why can't you ever be on time?	

Was it true?

On this occasion yes, but I am rarely late.	

How did you feel about the criticism?

Really upset.	

What did you say?

Sorry, I missed the bus.	

What was the response?

You've had all day to get here, why didn't you plan it better.	

What happened then?

I didn't speak for ages and felt really resentful.	

Did anything change as a result of this incident?

No.	

Receiving Criticism in my Professional Relationships

Think of a recent experience in your professional relationships (with a colleague, or a member of your work team) when you received criticism and dealt with it in an unsatisfactory way.

Describe the situation

Example	Your situation
I was held responsible for someone else's mistake in my department.	

What was said to you?

You should have checked her work.	

Was it true?

No – it wasn't my responsibility to check her work.	

How did you feel about the criticism?

It was completly unjustified. I was furious.	

What did you say?

Why can't you get your facts right before accusing people?	

What was the response?

Who do you think you are talking to?	

What happened then?

We both fumed for ages.	

Did anything change as a result of this incident?

The relationship got worse.	

Receiving Criticism Assertively

1. Listen carefully to the criticism keeping a sound inner dialogue e.g. "I may have made a mistake but it's nothing I can't put right". "Everyone makes mistakes at some time – I'm not superwoman".

2. If you are not clear exactly what the criticism is or why it is being given, ask for further explanation or clarification.

    Ask for examples (e.g. "I'd find it helpful, Lucy, if you could give me some examples of what you mean")

    It is important to do this assertively and not a challenging way

3. Think about what has been said.

    - is it justified?
    - is it partly justified?
    - is it completely unjustified?

4. If it is justified

    | a. | Acknowledge the truth – | Yes, I did forget the appointment |
    | b. | Explain how you feel – | I am extremely sorry that it happened |
    | c. | Try to empathise – | I realise that this must have been very annoying for you |

5. If it is **partly** justified

    | a. | Agree with the bit that is partly justified | Yes I was late this morning |
    | b. | Make it clear the rest is untrue | but I haven't been late **every** morning this week |
    | c. | Say how you feel | I feel disappointed that you think I've been in late all week |

6. When it is completely unjustified

   a. Reject the criticism use 'I' statements

   I don't accept that, or, on the contrary I've been in on time all week

   b. Add your positive thoughts

   I am a very good timekeeper

   c. Ask for an explanation

   Could you tell me why you think I've been late arriving?

7. If possible use the criticism to your advantage.

   ★ *Receive it with an open mind*

   ★ *Learn from other's views of you – does it give you insight into how your behaviour affects others?*

   ★ *Decide to change – if that would benefit you and others*

   ★ *Once you have thought about it, dealt with it, and learned from it*
      FORGET ABOUT IT

Now complete the exercise on dealing with criticism

Private Life

Refer back to the exercise on received criticism in your personal relationships on page 143.

Describe the situation

What was said?

Was it true?

What could you have said as an assertive reply?

What might have been the response?

What might have happened as a result?

Professional Life

Refer back to the exercise on received criticism in your professional relationships on page 144.

Describe the situation

```
```

What was said?

```
```

Was it true?

```
```

What could you have said as an assertive reply?

```
```

What might have been the response?

```
```

What might have happened as a result?

```
```

Handling Anger and Aggression from others

You are not on your own if you find it difficult to cope with aggression from other people. Many of us feel completely exhausted after a confrontation and spend hours going over the scene, reliving the experience and reawakening the feelings, fear, bitterness, humiliation, anger or frustration. When we next meet the individual or group, we may appear unconcerned, but often our resentment is still simmering away beneath the surface!

How do you react to aggression from others?

Do you become passive and crumple into a heap?

Do you rant and rave saying things you don't mean?

Do you freeze on the spot and become tongue-tied?

Do you apologise even though it isn't your fault?

Do you become manipulative or devious and deflect the person's aggression elsewhere?

Do you behave differently with work colleagues?

At home, you may react aggressively to your partner's anger but may become a timid mouse when a colleague shows his/her annoyance with you.

Private Life – Coping with Aggression

Of course it isn't possible to control other people's behaviour but we **can** control our reactions. It is vital that we maintain assertive behaviour in the face of other people's aggression otherwise **they** will start to control **our** behaviour

Example – How the other person's aggression may affect you

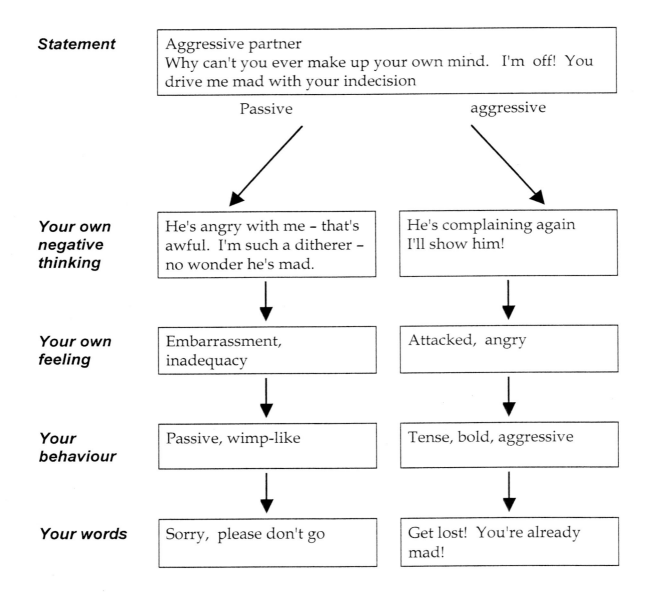

Statement	Aggressive partner Why can't you ever make up your own mind. I'm off! You drive me mad with your indecision	
	Passive	aggressive
Your own negative thinking	He's angry with me – that's awful. I'm such a ditherer – no wonder he's mad.	He's complaining again I'll show him!
Your own feeling	Embarrassment, inadequacy	Attacked, angry
Your behaviour	Passive, wimp-like	Tense, bold, aggressive
Your words	Sorry, please don't go	Get lost! You're already mad!

150

Professional Life – Coping with Aggression

Example – How the other person's aggression may affect you

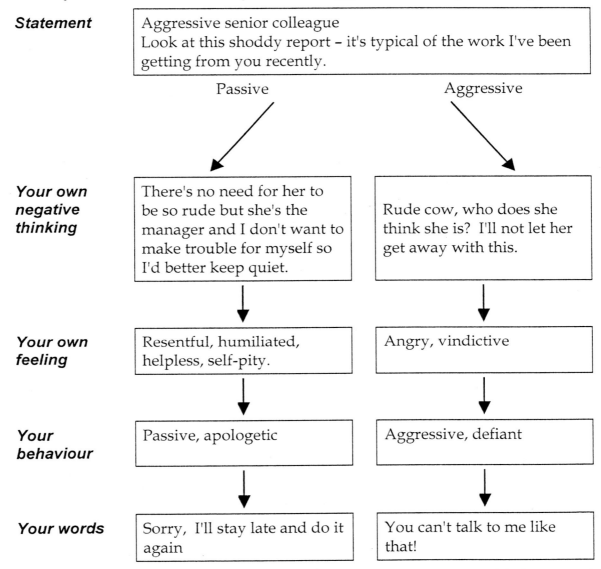

Statement

> Aggressive senior colleague
> Look at this shoddy report – it's typical of the work I've been getting from you recently.

Passive   Aggressive

Your own negative thinking

Passive	Aggressive
There's no need for her to be so rude but she's the manager and I don't want to make trouble for myself so I'd better keep quiet.	Rude cow, who does she think she is? I'll not let her get away with this.

Your own feeling

Passive	Aggressive
Resentful, humiliated, helpless, self-pity.	Angry, vindictive

Your behaviour

Passive	Aggressive
Passive, apologetic	Aggressive, defiant

Your words

Passive	Aggressive
Sorry, I'll stay late and do it again	You can't talk to me like that!

Relationships at work are often different from those in your private life because of the inequality in terms of power and authority, the issues of money and job security, and the complexity of coping with colleagues on both a personal and professional level. However, do remember not to take anger personally; colleagues may be angry as a result of frustration about a situation and the anger is not intentionally aimed at you. Other people may be aggressive towards you because this way of behaving makes them feel powerful and in control, whereas in reality they are feeling incompetent and insecure. If you are aware that bad temper and rudeness is one way of protecting a fragile self-esteem then you may feel more confident in asserting yourself.

It is important to learn to respond assertively to aggression and retain control of your own behaviour

Handling Aggression in my Private Life

Think about a difficult situation with your partner, close friend, family, acquaintance when you dealt ineffectively with someone's aggressive behaviour towards you.

Describe the situation

Describe the other person's behaviour

Describe how you felt

What were you thinking – **about yourself?**

– **about them?**

Describe your behaviour

Describe what you said

Describe what you would have liked to do and say

Handling Aggression in my Professional Life

Think about a difficult situation with work colleagues when you dealt ineffectively with aggressive behaviour towards you.

Describe the situation

Describe the other person's behaviour

Describe how you felt

What were you thinking   – about yourself?

– about them?

Describe your behaviour

Describe what you said

Describe what you would have liked to do and say

Guidelines on Responding Assertively to Aggression from others

The main aim is to stem the flow of anger in the other person, to get the interaction on the assertive–assertive level, so you can **both** deal with the issues and **both** feel happy about the interaction later.

To illustrate the approach we will use the previous example of the senior colleague complaining about the shoddy report.

Step 1

> ★ Take a deep breath
> ★ Count to 3 if this helps
> ★ Speak positively to yourself
> e.g.   I can stay calm
> I can deal with this

Before You Reply

Step 2

> ★ Listen carefully
> ★ Maintain good eye contact
> ★ Make sure your body language conveys your calm confident manner

Step 3

> ★ Make sure you understand what is being said
> ★ Ask for clarification and extra information
> ★ Listen to the responses
> ★ Keep your voice assertive

Jane, I don't think all my work has been shoddy recently. Can you tell me what else you've found unsatisfactory?

Step 4

(If aggression continues)

> ★ Say where you stand and how you feel
> ★ Remember to acknowledge the other person's position

I appreciate that you have found this latest report unsatisfactory. However, you haven't mentioned your concerns before and I do feel my previous work was satisfactory.

Step 5

(If aggression continues)

★   *Continue to restate your position*   ★   *Keep it short, firm and basic*

I recognise that you are angry with this report. However, you haven't complained about my work before which I feel was satisfactory.

Step 6

(If aggression continues)

★   *Indicate your negative feelings*   ★   *Say what you would like to happen*

Jane, I feel disappointed and angry that you can make such a general criticism of my work based on one report. I'd like to take some time to look at the report and discuss this later with you as well as my general progress.

Coping assertively with aggressive behaviour is very demanding but it is well worth the effort.

Remember to slow down your responses – listen – and stay calm. Repeat your message and this technique (called the broken record technique) will keep you from being side tracked.

In the following checklist we have listed some common types of everyday aggressive remarks which you may have to respond to. Fill in the two spaces with your own example from page 152 then practise your own assertive responses to the rest of the examples given.

155

Coping with Everyday Aggressive Remarks

Type of aggressive comment	Example	Your assertive reply
Your own example from your private life		
Your own example from your professional life		
Nagging	How much longer do I have to wait for you	Is there a problem with the time we have to leave?
Suggesting you are stretching the truth	Oh don't give me that – that isn't what you said	That's certainly what I remember saying
Using emotional language to describe what you've done	That was a stupid thing to do It was utterly thoughtless that you didn't phone	I'm not happy with what I do, but I don't think its stupid I accept it would have been more convenient if I'd phoned but I can't agree it was utterly thoughtless
Tell you what to do	What I'd do if I were you is to leave that job and get one nearer home that you can cope with better	I appreciate your concern but I think I'm the right person to decide
Insulting labels	That's a typical woman's reaction	It's my reaction and it's up to me to judge my behaviour
Questioning your choice	Are you sure this evening dress is the right one for you?	It feels all right for me at the moment

4

Managing Your Private and Professional Life

Developing Management Skills

Introduction

Being more assertive in your relationships with other people will have helped you to recognise the value of being clear about what you want, and in planning ahead what you are going to say for effective communication. You can gradually build on these basic assertive skills to develop a more structured approach in dealing with other changes you want to make in your life. Life can often seem so complicated and you may feel that simply surviving requires considerable expertise in personal management!

> *Do you have a clear idea of your personal and professional priorities?*
>
> *Do you frequently miss out on things because you haven't got time?*
>
> *Are you fulfilling your potential?*
>
> *Do you manage to take regular exercise?*
>
> *Are you getting real satisfaction from your career?*

To realise your potential and to go for a wider programme of change in your private and professional life, you need

   *   more highly developed and sensitive personal management skills.

   *   a positive strategic approach to making changes

Developing good management skills must become a top priority in working towards personal and professional fulfilment.

What are Management Skills?

Management skills are not skills reserved for those in high powered executive positions. We can **all** benefit from developing management skills in our personal and professional life. Management skills are to do with planning and organising, achieving goals, making things happen. They are also about gaining satisfaction from the tasks, realising your potential and enjoying life to the full. The last point is most important. It is no use being organised and efficient if you are not getting out of life what you want and (in so far as is possible) doing things the way **you** want to do them. Many of us spend so much time dealing with other people's lives that we lose sight of where we are going.

An important first step in applying management skills to your life at home and at work must be to spend time identifying your needs and what is important to you.

Management skills include:

* Being clear about where you are, where you want to go and being aware of the choices open to you.

* Being able to motivate other people to aid you – friends, family or colleagues.

* Being able to choose options wisely.

* Being able to prioritise.

* Being able to plan time, to organise yourself and others.

* Being able to delegate to others efficiently.

* Being flexible in your approach so that you can adapt easily to changing circumstances.

Many people mistakenly assume that spontaneity disappears when you develop good management skills. Nothing is further from the truth. You will become far more open and relaxed and have more time to enjoy yourself because you will have planned your time.

How Good are Your Management Skills?

Put a ✔ in the appropriate column.
Turn to next page to check your score

Do you ...

	Never	Sometimes	Often	Always
1. Write a list of things that must be done today?				
2. Refuse to take work home at weekends or in the evening on a regular basis?				
3. Say 'no' to unscheduled interruptions?				
4. Delegate easily and efficiently?				
5. Put tasks in order of priority and work on them in that order?				
6. Meet deadlines without any real hassle, e.g. staying up half the night?				
7. Arrive on time for appointments?				
8. Plan time to give feedback and information to people who work for you on a regular basis?				
9. Think about where you want to be in your career in 5 years time?				
10. Change ideas/plans easily when difficulties arise?				
11. Remember other people's birthdays, anniversaries etc?				
12. Shop systematically i.e. once a month, once a week?				
13. Take regular exercise?				
14. Have your car regularly serviced?				
15. Keep an up-to-date, well ordered file of personal affairs, bank statements, insurance etc?				
16. Watch only those TV programmes you've planned to watch?				
17. Have a place for everything so that you don't spend time looking for things?				
18. Have a system for knowing when stocks run low so that you don't run out of stamps, salt, loo roll etc?				
19. Enjoy leisure time with partner, family without feeling preoccupied?				
20. Have social events planned well ahead in your diary that **you** have organised?				

How Good are Your Management Skills –
Results of Questionnaire.

Score: Always   5
          Often   3
          Sometimes   1
          Never   0

Your total score

80–100   You have excellent management skills which you apply well at home and at work. Your clear thinking, efficiency and ability to plan ahead mean that you make the most of your present job and gain real satisfaction from your social life. However, you have the drive, energy and determination to meet even greater challenges.

55–79   Your management skills are good and you generally have a clear view of where you are and what you want to do. Occasionally your plans go wrong and things don't work as well as you expected but these hiccups are rare. You are likely to enjoy a management role. Are you realising your potential in your career?

26–54   Sometimes you sail through the day and everything goes to plan. At other times you find you've mislaid something important, forgotten to cancel an order, put off phoning someone 'till tomorrow'. It is important to have an overview of your life at home and at work and focus on the problematic areas. You could find yourself with more time and energy to do what you most enjoy.

0–25   You find managing your private and professional life a real chore at times. You swing from feeling angry and depressed about things to being resigned to a life that often seems chaotic. You **can** learn management skills. Start by dealing with **one** thing that you've been putting off for ages - for example clearing your desk top of unnecessary clutter, or writing a letter to the insurance company. Take one step at a time and you'll gradually feel less hassled.

The first ten questions on the questionnaire are concerned with your management skills at work, the remaining questions with your management skills at home. It may be useful to see if your management skills are stronger in one area than another. Could you transfer some of the management strategies you use at work to your home life and vice versa?

Managing Your Career

Are you getting the happiness, satisfaction, stimulation, self-respect and financial reward that you deserve from your job? Many women are not and spend years working in unsatisfying, underpaid jobs where their talents remain dormant. This happens to many women because they remain unsure of their personal needs and wants.

> **The key to getting what you want, or making things more satisfactory for yourself, is to be clear about what you want in the first place.**
>
> *If you don't know where you are going, you'll possibly end up somewhere else!*

What are your needs and wants in your working life?

In the chart provided on the next page simply list by brainstorming all the 'needs' and 'wants' you can think of connected with your career. These may be things you want to achieve, things you want to happen, things you'd like to do (now and in the future). Write as long a list as you can. Write down *everything* from the mundane to the preposterous.

Examples: I'd like to change my job but I don't know what else to do.
I'd like to become a professional musician.
I'd like to be happy in my work.
I'd like to study for a new career.
I'd like a job nearer home.

When you have completed your list put a letter (after each statement) which denotes by which time you would like to achieve these objectives: S for soon, Y for within the next year, or F for sometime in the future.

Next, number your objectives 1, 2, or 3, depending on how important each one is to you.

Needs and wants in my working life

	Priority 1, 2, or 3	'Needs' and 'Wants'	Time S, Y, or F
1	2	*Example: I'd like to change my job*	*S*
2			
3			
4			
5			
6			
7			
8			
9			
10			
11			
12			
13			
14			
15			

When you have completed your list (work quickly and don't agonise over choices), write your objectives graded 1 in the space below. Try to place these in rank order.

My immediate priorities are:

This is the first stage in your career planning. Often this is as far as people get because their objectives or goals remain too daunting, too obscure or too ambitious.

You need to make each goal

☆   measurable
☆   realistic
☆   clear
☆   specific
☆   set in a reasonable time frame.

E.g.   *"I need to organise better the time spent phoning customers."*

This is far too general. Change this to:

"From next week I will set aside a specific time each day to make phone calls to customers."

E.g.   *"I want to get promotion as soon as possible so I will discuss this with my boss."*

This is too vague and may well remain an intention for months! Change this to:

"I will ask my boss tomorrow to arrange a meeting within the next two weeks when I can discuss my career prospects with him."

Setting goals is important because

☆   they help us to define what we want
☆   they give us a sense of direction
☆   they give us a sense of motivation
☆   they give us a chance to concentrate our time and energy on something specific.

It is important to realise that our goals are constantly changing. We need to take time every few months to have a fresh look at our goals in terms of importance and priority, and to set new goals.

Force-Field Analysis

In any situation where we wish to make a change there will be some forces working against the change – things which weaken our resolve, and other forces which work towards the change and help us achieve our objective.

You will improve your chances of achieving your goal if you can identify and work on these helping and hindering forces *before* you move into action.

Example

The following diagram represents the forces working for and against Anne's goal which is:

. . . . to ask for more responsibility in my job at my annual appraisal next week.

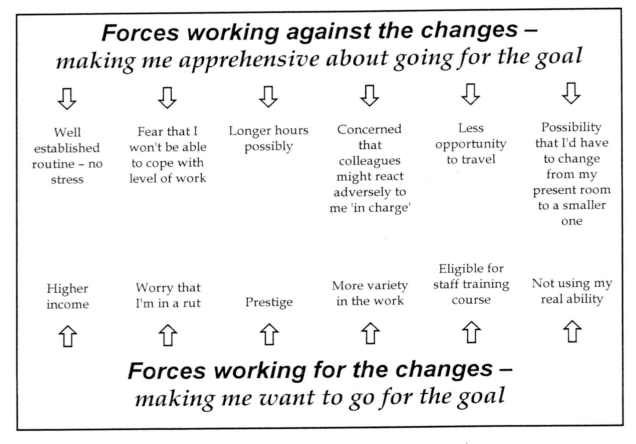

Now write the goal which you have chosen as a priority. State what you want to achieve very specifically. Start with the word 'to ...' and make sure you include a date by which you hope to achieve it.

My goal is to ...

I hope to achieve this by ...

On the chart provided below

1. List all the forces working in *favour* of what you want to achieve. Be specific (who, what, when, how much). *Circle the most important ones in green.*

2. List all the forces working *against* what you want to achieve. Be specific. *Circle the most important ones in red.*

Forces working against the changes –
making me apprehensive about going for the goal

⇩   ⇩   ⇩   ⇩   ⇩   ⇩

⇧   ⇧   ⇧   ⇧   ⇧   ⇧

Forces working for the changes –
making me want to go for the goal

Work on each force in turn. Start with the circled ones.

Find ways to strengthen the positives.

Example

One of Anne's forces pushing her towards her goal was

– eligible for staff training courses.

She could increase the strength of this positive by getting the programme of courses available next year – choosing those which interested her and browsing through reading material suggested on the course reading lists.

Find ways to weaken the effect of the negatives.

Example

One of Anne's 'negatives' was

– concern that she would have to change rooms.

She might decide that she would bring this up at the meeting with her boss and discuss the feasibility of retaining her original room.

Sometimes you may have to write 'no action possible' if you cannot find a way of reducing or increasing the effect of one of your forces.

Developing an Action Plan

Having defined clearly what you want and need, and identified the helping and hindering forces, your next step is to find a way to make it happen by developing an *ACTION PLAN*.

Using the step-by-step guide below, fill in your Action Plan on the next page

1.	State your goal.

2.	Start with what *you* are going to do *now*.

3.	Think about the positive action steps you will need to take. Write them all down in any order. Writing them down will help you to see that one action step, e.g. I must write my CV next week, will involve you in planning a prior one, e.g. I will buy a book on writing CVs tomorrow after work.

4.	Rearrange the steps into a logical order.

5.	Put a date into your action plan when you are going to review your progress towards your goal.

6.	Give yourself a realistic deadline.

☆	*When you have completed your action plan, transfer the dates to your diary to remind you of the step deadlines.*

☆	*Involve others, family, friends, work colleagues to help you to stick to your action plan.*

☆	*If circumstances change or things don't work out as originally planned, don't abandon the action plan, just re-work your schedules.*

Action Plan

My goal is . . . .

Action steps I need to take
(write them in any order)

Action steps in sequence

Step 1 to . . .

    I will start this on ....(date)

Step 2 to . . .

    I will start this on ....(date)

Step 3 to . . .

    I will start this on ....(date)

Step 4 to . . .

    I will start this on ....(date)

I will review my progress on ....(date)

I should know whether I have achieved my goal by ....(date)

Managing Your Career Change

Many women consider a change of career, but then become overwhelmed by all the negative forces they see as preventing the change.

Example

'I don't know what other kind of career I would be suited to'

'I don't think there would be any jobs available in this area for someone without experience'

'The recession has made changing careers impossible'

Negative ideas and attitudes such as these may act as such powerful deterrents that we don't even consider an action plan!

What steps could you take to reduce the negative effect of these forces which dampen motivation and leave many women shilly-shallying for years in unrewarding jobs?

Boost your motivation by considering some of the following ideas:

Positive Action Steps to discover what kind of career you would be suited to and what might be available locally.

Step 1   Spend an evening next week assessing your skills and interests

It is essential to know the range of skills that we do well so that we can have a base on which to build and develop a career. Think about the skills you use informally and everyday – those abilities which are to do with your personality and natural aptitudes rather than work-content skills. Do you enjoy working with people, things, information or ideas (or a combination of these)?

People who have skills in the different areas are likely to do certain types of job better than others.

Identify your skills from the following chart.

Ideas

People who have abilities with ideas are likely to perform best in work in which they have to be creative, original, innovative. The fields could be in literature, art, music, but they could do well in other occupations where they could be imaginative and engaged in abstract thinking.

People

People who have abilities with others are likely to be good at influencing, directing, or organising other people, e.g. motivating, selling, persuading, teaching, entertaining. They may have skills in supporting others – in advising, caring, counselling work, helping others to work things through.

Things

People who have abilities with things are likely to work best in occupations where they use tools, machinery, vehicles. They may have skills in making, repairing, servicing equipment, and in knowing how things work.

Information

People who have skills with information are able to organise facts and data systematically. They would be good at recording and evaluating information. They are often good at getting things sorted and into order, be it figures, routines or systems.

Think about your interests too

Are these:

Practical	Making things, crafts, hobbies, gardening, sport.
Investigative	Intellectual challenge games, fact-gathering, interests in geology, biology.
Artistic	Language, drama, art, music.
Social	People, training, caring, voluntary work.
Enterprising	Setting up groups motivating others, new projects.
Administrative/ Organisational	Organising activities, secretarial interests, computing, word-processing.

Do these interests give you ideas about the careers you would enjoy?

Step 2   Spend time during the next month in your local area researching career ideas further

Make an appointment at the local Job Centre/local Careers Office. The Job Centre may offer you a computer analysis of your aptitudes. Use books, computer software, library resources, local Careers Office resources so that you can develop your background knowledge of occupations and get a broader picture of the range of things you could consider.

You need this knowledge to work out what options you have, what is open to you, what retraining you may need. Ask friends, colleagues, career guidance organisations for extra advice.

Steps 3 – 7

☆   Write to personnel departments of companies which interest you to find out what vacancies exist.

☆   Use personal contacts, friends and relatives working in the target companies to find out about job opportunities.

☆   Check Yellow Pages for names of private agencies and consultancies.

☆   Find out about the level of local vacancies and general recruitment policies by approaching professional organisations and unions for literature and information.

☆   Try speculative applications.

Giving Your Present Job a Management Boost

For many women a career change is neither possible nor desirable. However, it is important to consider how you could apply some of the management techniques discussed in relation to career change, to gain greater satisfaction from your present job.

Listed below are some suggestions for you to think about in relation to your present career. Space has been left for you to add your own ideas in each of the categories. Try to be specific.

Improving job satisfaction in my present job	
Improving individual motivation	
Could you:	**Possibilities in my present job**
Ask for more responsibility	
Ask if certain tasks could be delegated	
Go on staff training courses	
★ skills training	
★ assertiveness training	
★ stress management	
★ women into management	
Take external courses	
e.g. OU courses, night school	
Become more assertive with senior/ junior colleagues	
Become more assertive in groups and meetings	
Organise your time better	
Prepare more thoroughly to make presentations, meetings and dealing with others less stressful	
Equip yourself with a new image. Find a style which builds your confidence	
Ensure that you make full use of the appraisal system	

Improving staff relationships	
Could we:	
Organise more social activities for staff	
Allocate regular dates for staff meetings	
Develop a support system for new staff	
Run team-building courses	
Ask for outside speakers to discuss sensitive issues	
Ask for more support staff	
Help to develop a friendlier atmosphere by celebrating staff birthdays and other special occasions	

Improving working environment	
Could we:	
Suggest an improvement in the catering facilities, e.g. coffee machines, fridge, microwave, new cups	
Campaign for an up-to-date computer, telephone system, better service contracts on equipment	
Make better use of existing resources, e.g. training sessions for using present facilities more effectively	
Raise concerns about central heating, fresh air, lighting, furniture, general working conditions	

This exercise may stimulate your ideas and help you to recognise that <u>you</u> can take action either on your own or by approaching the relevant person

Manage Your Time in Your Private and Professional Life

Time management is often associated with work but you will gain real benefits in your personal, social and family life as well by using your time more effectively. This doesn't mean you should be planning activities for every minute of your life. However, a more organised lifestyle means extra hours to spend and more energy to use. Think how much you miss because you 'never get round to it'. Weekends away which you've been promising yourself, learning a language, updating computer skills, taking up yoga, reading that book recommended by a friend several months ago. Time management is very much concerned with planning for things you **want** to do as well as things you **must** do.

The busier you are and the more involved you become in a variety of enterprises at work and at home, the more important is an overview of your life. To make a start on planning your time more effectively you need to be aware of how you presently use your time – this knowledge is the first step in learning to manage time. On the next page you will find an outline weekly time log. Over the next week fill in a detailed record of how you spend your time in your private and professional life. Make your entries regularly – at least twice a day – as memories can be very unreliable.

Weekly Time Log

	Mon	Tues	Wed	Thurs	Fri	Sat	Sun
10–12							
8–10							
6–8							
4–6							
2–4							
12–2							
10–12							
8–10							
6–8							
4–6							
2–4							
12–2							

Daily Time Log

Although keeping a time log can be tedious it is an extremely important tool for finding out exactly how long things take, and where time gets lost. On a couple of days during the week try to complete a more detailed record of your daily activities from the time you arrive at work until the time you leave. (It is important to fill in everything you do – social chats, coffee breaks, interruptions – everything). Record your use of time on the chart below.

Time	Activity	Time Spent

Weekly Activity Chart

When you have completed the chart you will be able to analyse exactly how your time was spent. Fill in the 'activity chart' below so that you can see more clearly which activities took up major portions of your time. Try to estimate, in one week, how long you spent on each activity. A few common activities are listed as a start.

Activity	Hours Spent
Sleeping	
Travelling	
Eating	
Shopping	
Household tasks	
Watching TV	

Review of Last Week's Use of Time

You will, no doubt, have some surprises in the way you have used your time in the week under review. Use the questionnaire to give you further insight into your use of time. Circle the appropriate answer.

1.   How much time did I waste approximately during the week?

Hours

	0	4	8	12	16	20	24	28	32	36	40	more
Private Life	0	4	8	12	16	20	24	28	32	36	40	more
Professional Life	0	4	8	12	16	20	24	28	32	36	40	more

2.   How organised was I each day in knowing what I wanted to achieve?

	Completely	Mostly	Slightly	Not at all
Private Life	Completely	Mostly	Slightly	Not at all
Professional Life	Completely	Mostly	Slightly	Not at all

3.   How much time have I spent on what I enjoy during this week in my private life?

Hours	0	4	8	12	16	20	24	28	32	36	40	more
	0	4	8	12	16	20	24	28	32	36	40	more

4.   Could I cut down on the time spent travelling?

	Yes	No
Private Life	Yes	No
Professional Life	Yes	No

5.   Did I use the time I spent travelling, waiting for appointments etc, constructively

	Yes	No
Private Life	Yes	No
Professional Life	Yes	No

6. Have I procrastinated about things I have to do?

Private Life	Yes	No
Professional Life	Yes	No

7. Have I spent time on activities which could have been done by someone else?

Private Life	Yes	No
Professional Life	Yes	No

8. Do I need to attend all the meetings I go to?

Private Life	Yes	No
Professional Life	Yes	No

9. On whom or what am I spending too much time?

Private Life	
Professional Life	

10. On whom or what am I spending too little time?

Private Life	
Professional Life	

You may have found that many of the things which would give you real satisfaction in your private and professional life are squeezed out by other activities. The second step in managing your time more effectively is to decide what you would **like** to do and balance these against what you **must** do.

Think about some of the things you would like to do next week at home and at work. Keep in mind your committed time so that you don't become too ambitious with your list. Write down all activities in the space provided below. Try to prioritise.

Things I would like to do next week	
Private Life	**Professional Life**
1.	1.
2.	2.
3.	3.
4.	4.

Copy out this list and put it up somewhere you can see it frequently during the week.

List-making is best carried out on a daily basis. It is best to draw up your list at the end of the day and, as you have done in this exercise above, list all the things you have to do and all the things you want to do during the next day. You may find that two separate lists help, especially if you have a busy working day and hectic social life too.

Private Life	Things I want to do tomorrow
Private Life	Things I have to do tomorrow
Professional Life	Things I want to do tomorrow
Professional Life	Things I have to do tomorrow

Code each of your items   'U' Urgent
                                    'I' Important
                                    'W' Can wait

Put the items on your list into order of priority the 'U's first, then the 'I's and then the 'W's.

As you go through the day complete the 'U's first then the 'I's and finally the 'W's. cross them off your list as you complete them – this acts as a reward.

At the end of the day transfer to tomorrow's list any uncompleted item. As it goes on to tomorrow's list it may move from a 'W' to an 'I'.

You will want to adapt your list making it suit your own needs. Don't forget to allow 20% extra time for such jobs as report writing, shopping or making phone calls. If you persevere you will find list-making and prioritising in this way a very powerful tool in managing your time.

It is best to transfer your list to a planner or diary. Try to draw up your list for the next day the evening before. If you get into a regular routine of doing this it soon becomes second nature. You can buy an expensive filo fax but most diaries can be adapted in the following way:

Friday		To Do (work)	
9.00	Mail	Minutes for meeting	U
9.30 ⬍	Prepare references	Check report for tomorrow	I
10.30		Talk to John about new client	W
13.00 ⬍	Lunch Anne – Hare and Hounds		
14.00			
14.30	Phone calls		
16.30 ⬍	Planning meeting		
17.30			
		To Do (home)	
20.00	Paul and Jill for supper	Buy salad	U
		Organise dog for next weekend	I

Try to follow this pattern for a week and at the end of the week review your progress.

Identify Your Time Waster

With the best will in the world you may still find time management skills difficult to implement. Try to identify any time wasters from the list below which apply to you and work out how you might deal with them.

I get side-tracked easily and spend too much time on trivial tasks	→ *Make clear goals and action plans with times allocated and stick to them.*
I spend ages looking for papers, sellotape, books etc	→ *Tidy your desk drawers and make sure everything has a place. Decide on a filing system which you can cope with.*
I seem to waste hours on trains, buses, waiting for appointments	→ *Use waiting time constructively. Always carry pen, paper, book. Plan ideas and organise activities.*
I take on too much and find it hard to say 'no'	→ *Learn assertive skills. Learn to delegate more work to others.*
I'm always rushing and don't seem to do anything properly	→ *Write out your 'to do' list adding 25% extra time for jobs. Stick to your planned order.*
I seem to be too much of a perfectionist even with mundane jobs like ironing	→ *Learn to relax your standards. You may be wasting your most creative hours doing routine tasks too well.*
People interrupt me at home and at work or stay chatting longer than I have time for	→ *Make sure people know when you don't want to be disturbed. Be assertive in saying 'I must get my work done'. Use answerphones more. Write short notes or use e-mail instead of phoning, to avoid getting drawn into long conversations.*
I get overwhelmed by all I have to do and often end up completing little	→ *Prioritise. Make sure you do your 'urgent' jobs first and work steadily through your list.*
I seem to have more clutter to deal with than other people	→ *Handle a piece of paper only once – file it, deal with it or bin it. Regularly sort out desk drawers so that you keep a check on items and things to discard that you don't need. Don't wait till it becomes a huge task.*
I often feel too tired or tense to get my work done efficiently, or use time creatively in the evenings	→ *Identify your 'best' time of the day for the most difficult tasks. Take regular breaks throughout the day. Don't be tempted to work through lunch or coffee. Consider paying for extra help – labour-saving equipment, secretarial help, cleaning help. Buy easily prepared food.*

Manage Your Leisure Activities

Many women have difficulty in giving leisure an adequate space in their lives. However, it should take a high priority and needs to be planned for in the same way as work and home management.

Complete the following exercise on your use of leisure time.

Work out approximately how many hours of leisure you have in an average week. Fill in the pie chart below to indicate how these are spent.

Example

Your use of leisure time

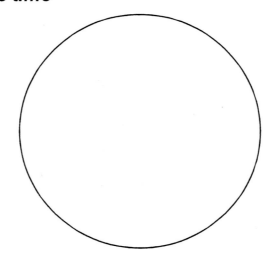

With a coloured pen shade in the activities which you most enjoy. Shade in the activities which you least enjoy. Are you spending your leisure time doing the things you **really** want to do.

Fill in the next pie chart to indicate the people with whom you spend time.

Example

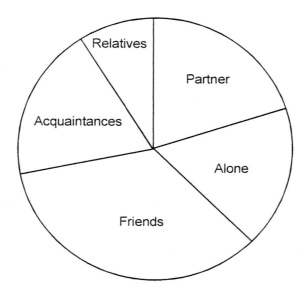

Your leisure relationships

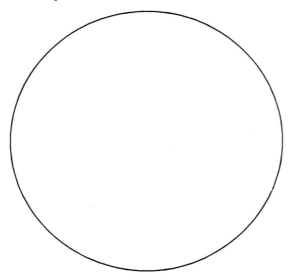

Are you spending time with people whose company you most enjoy?

It is vital that your leisure time should give you maximum pleasure. Enjoyment is essential.

Write down three things which annoy you about your use of leisure time in a typical week.

Examples

Do you spend your time looking after everyone else's interests? Are you a slave to TV? Are you too houseproud? Do you have sufficient time for leisure? Are you too tired to use leisure time well? Do you decide to do things at the last minute and become disappointed because all tickets have gone, the restaurant is full, or friends are busy? Have you sufficient hobbies and interests?

1.

2.

3.

Write down one thing which you intend to stop doing next week.

Write down one thing which you would like to do instead.

Consider this as a personal goal and write this activity in next week's diary. This is as important for your personal well-being as a work goal.

Set yourself the task of doing one **new** leisure activity each week for the next four weeks. Identify what type of activity you most enjoy.

* being with people

* being alone

* taking exercise

* being creative

* being competitive

* being entertained

* travelling

* studying new topics

Get ideas of what is available locally from friends, the local paper, library facilities.

Read the following section. Explore ideas and think about the choices you could make to ensure your leisure becomes more fulfilling.

* Relaxation for many women means doing something completely different from their work. Have you a sedentary job, a thinking job? Perhaps a physical activity, a creative hobby working with your hands would offer a change? Have you a job where you are always on the move? Perhaps an interest which allows you to sit back and be entertained, concerts, theatre, music, sport events, would be appropriate.

* Often deciding to do things on the last minute leads to disappointment. Plan ahead. Season tickets for concerts, theatre etc, are worth considering. Decide to do something on a regular basis with a group of friends; once a month for a pub meal out together for example. Take turns to decide on the venue.

* Plan a night away every so often. Try to find a place which you have never visited and research places of interest in the area.

* Plan a regular treat for yourself at the end of each month – a massage, facial, or pedicure, a new book, tape or video. It is important to look after yourself in this way.

* Make a specific evening each month a 'family evening'. Plan something different each time, an unusual meal, a new game, a favourite video, an evening 'with a theme'.

* Try to get away for a weekend every few months with family, partner, friends or alone. A change of scene is enormously beneficial for everyone. Sometimes being with a new group of people on an 'activity weekend' is a real energiser. Find out what's available from learning to build a dry stone wall in Yorkshire to bird watching in Devon.

Leisure activities I intend to develop in the future
1.
2.
3.
4.

Programme Review

Now you have reached the end of this Personal Power Workbook in which you have looked at various aspects of your life from a new perspective. You have learned and practised a number of strategies and techniques to help you determine what you want to do and how to achieve the changes you have now decided you need. Run down the list of topics covered in the programme. Think about the significance of each of the topics in developing your potential in your private and professional life; tick the appropriate column to determine where you will need to take action.

	I am happy with this	I need to work on this
Building Self-Esteem		
Understanding the importance of self-esteem		
How my self-esteem affects my life		
Challenging negative beliefs about myself		
Knowing what my positive qualities and strengths are		
Enhancing my self-esteem at home		
Enhancing my self-esteem at work		
Setting goals to maintain my self-esteem		
Dealing with Stress		
Recognising areas of stress in my life		
How stress affects me emotionally and physically		
Understanding how to take positive action to deal with stress		
Designing a programme of physical exercise to reduce stress		

Giving myself time to pursue hobbies, interest, relaxation techniques etc.		
Feeling confident to cope with stressful situations		
Stress-proofing myself for the future		
Developing Assertiveness		
Being assertive with my partner		
Being assertive with my family and friends		
Being assertive with work colleagues		
Asking for what I want		
Refusing requests		
Giving praise and compliments assertively		
Handling criticism & aggression from others		
Managing my lifestyle		
Managing my career		
Managing my career change		
Setting realistic goals		
Developing action plans		
Giving my present job a management boost		
Managing my time in my professional life		
Managing my time in my private life		
Managing my leisure activities		

You may be feeling inspired and enthusiastic to put everything into practice at once! But do remember to start small and choose realistic goals. You may find that you need to refresh your memory from time to time; just revisit some of the chapters you found most useful.

We hope that you have enjoyed working through this self-development workbook and that you have real success in achieving personal power and fulfilling your private and professional life.

Good Luck With The NEW You

Further Publications and Training

If you have enjoyed this book and think that your organisation would like to host a personal development course, you may like further details of our training.

- The guidance and exercises in this book are brought powerfully to life in our one-day or two-day **Personal Power** courses.

  Explore personal effectiveness safely within a lively programme, expertly facilitated by one of our trainers. Our team consistently receive high scores in post-course feedback and are known for their warm, practical approach spiced with honesty and humour.

  Participants are led gently through self-awareness exploration and are inspired to try new effective approaches, make clear action plans for the future and take away a range of practical techniques for a more empowered future.

  For more information or an informal discussion, contact our Project Manager by one of the means listed overleaf.

Two further publications by Jenny Mosley and Eileen Gillibrand are available and can be ordered by post or via our website.

- **She Who Dares Wins**

  An extended version of the Personal Power workbook, taking the four themes of self-esteem, stress, assertiveness and management skills and developing them further. In addition to the self-assessment exercises, clear diagrams and examples concisely capture the learning points for you to consider before setting goals and practising the techniques to fulfil your potential.

- **Boost Your Energy** – a working mother's guide to balancing home and work

  Pressures and expectations have never been more extreme for working mothers, as the dilemmas and drains upon energy multiply. In her foreword, Anita Roddick of the Body Shop comments that it is time to 'celebrate the working mother', and the authors help us do just that. From personal experience and with insight they expose some of the subtle pressures that can eat away at the working mother's balance, and give clear practical advice on how to turn these around. From harnessing your beliefs to developing personal care plans and using smart strategies at work and with your children, this book will help you re-prioritise how to 'spend' your energy and show you how to have more to spend. (Previously published as *When I Go to Work I Feel Guilty*.)

■ Resources for Schools

Additionally, Jenny Mosley and her team offer an extensive range of self-esteem based courses, publications and products specifically designed for schools, based on her **Whole School Quality Circle Time Model** which has revolutionised the approach to self-esteem and behaviour management at all ages. With increasing interest internationally, Quality Circle Time has been rapidly growing in use in the UK since 1980 and is recognised by educational leaders as a very effective way forward in schools. See our latest catalogue for full details.

To order books, request a catalogue or obtain further information on training courses, please contact us in any of the following ways. We look forward to hearing from you.

Jenny Mosley Consultancies
8 Westbourne Road
Trowbridge
Wiltshire
BA14 0AJ
England

Telephone 01225 767157
Fax 01225 755631
E-mail: circletime@jennymosley.demon.co.uk
Website: www. jennymosley.demon.co.uk